HOUS
DIVIDING

HOW TO CREATE MULTIPLE HOMES
FROM A SINGLE PROPERTY

PAUL HYMERS

NEW
HOLLAND

Dedication

For my daughters Karina and Rochelle, my nephews Ian, Ashley, Richard and William, and indeed to all those waiting to find independence in their own home.

First published in 2007 by New Holland Publishers (UK) Ltd
Garfield House, 86–88 Edgware Road
London W2 2EA
London • Cape Town • Sydney • Auckland
www.newhollandpublishers.com

ISBN 978 184537 9582

Senior Editor: Naomi Waters
Copy-editor: Siobhan O' Connor
Designer: Casebourne Rose Design Associates
Illustrator: Sue Rose
Cover photograph: Sue Rose
Production: Hema Gohil

Printed and bound by Replika Press, India

Declaration

Acknowledgements
Thanks as always to my colleagues in Building Control, Development Control, Forward Planning, Conservation, Environmental Health and Housing. In particular, Adrian, Chris, Clive, Martin, Maxine, Paul, Peter, Rachel, Robin, Rod and Steve.
Thank you also to Nigel Bonnage and Steve Green Limited for their architectural design services. And all those I've met engaged in home dividing over the past few years. It can't have been easy for any of you.

Contents

Introduction

The motivation for dividing a property into smaller homes is not hard to find. Demand for housing continues to outstrip supply and, as for the cost of homes, the statistics are bewildering.

Creating an annexe to the home is not only desirable, but becoming almost essential – and not just for the grandparents. The children who have reached adulthood only to discover they have as much chance of going to the moon as they have of buying a starter home are needing annexes, too. An annexe converted from a garage or divided off from another part of the home can become a self-contained space, with its own entrance and shared facilities, at modest expense. The basic facilities of independence do not require a lot of room. A separate entrance door, a shower with a toilet, and a lounge/bedroom will do the trick. Designed and built from new as a detached garden building or linked extension, an annexe can achieve complete independence with its own supplied services of gas, water and electricity. It will be a separate home in every respect but market value.

For the more ambitious, dividing into apartments or maisonettes not only creates the space for independent living, but also fills a need for those climbing the first rungs of the property ladder. In the final decades of the twentieth century, the trend for large 'executive' home building was in full swing, with detached four- and five-bedroom homes extravagantly built over half-acre plots, complete with detached luxury garages to match. Today, all that has changed. Few developers build executive homes – instead they build smaller and higher, in ever decreasing footprints. What we need now are apartments and maisonettes, but land for building new apartment blocks is both at a premium and in short supply. Large existing homes, however, are plentiful. Those of the Victorian and Edwardian eras are perfect for dividing into smaller homes, but there is just as much potential waiting to be unlocked in larger modern homes. Here, for the home divider there is not only the chance to create an independent home for adult children or elderly parents, but also the opportunity to realise the full potential and ultimate value of your property.

CHAPTER 1

Homes in the United Kingdom

Life has changed, and the demand for smaller homes, fuelled by smaller families, single occupiers and single parents, has taken over from executive house building.

Small apartments represent the first rung on the property ladder for most people; however, in 2007, the average cost of that first rung was eight times the average annual salary. Often, of course, young adults are earning salaries below the average. Also, the average house price broke through the £200,000 barrier in the same year, just seven years after it had reached the £100,000 mark. The house-price graph for the United Kingdom now looks like a global-warming prediction. What had been a steady rise since the early 1980s of £2000 to £3000 a year ended around 1996–97, and since then price rises have leapt forwards in ever increasing bounds.

Coupled with this acceleration in property value, we have seen another change in the way we live. In the 1960s, half of all households were families, but now for the first time more people are living alone (or as a single parent) than in a larger family. This fact first emerged in 2002, but the trend has only continued since, increasing the demand for smaller homes. Whether built from new or divided from existing buildings, small homes now represent the United Kingdom's most rapid growth in construction. Between 2002 and 2006, the quantity of apartments being constructed each year grew by 48 per cent. At the same time, the construction of large homes has fizzled away – so much so that, by 2006, 47 per cent of all new homes were apartments. Apartments satisfy a need for low-cost, affordable accommodation and can even help to regenerate some urban areas. The large houses and buildings that are suited to dividing into apartments are often in urban areas with good transport links and facilities in walking distance. That makes them sustainable homes, ideal for young and old alike. Often these large terraced or semi-detached properties are within Conservation Areas, and the repair work inherent in dividing homes can also help to restore and maintain them for the future. Conversely, some tourist areas, typical in seaside towns, have seen guesthouses sold off to property developers and divided into homes, and entire roads have been given over to flat conversions.

By 2010, the Government aims to have helped 100,000 first-time buyers and key workers on to the property ladder by using shared ownership schemes with housing associations. Projects to divide homes play a large part in supplying this demand.

Of course, not all homes are suited to division as self-contained flats or maisonettes, but there are still options with those that are not. Small- and medium-sized family homes are typically terraced or semi-detached, but fulfil a valuable role in housing families; their loss to smaller single-person accommodation may be unacceptable to local planning authorities. As family homes, however, they might be extended to provide annexed accommodation for family members.

APARTMENT 4

APARTMENT 3

APARTMENT 2

APARTMENT 1

BATHROOM

BATHROOM

◀ Large Victorian homes lend themselves to dividing if their character can be maintained.

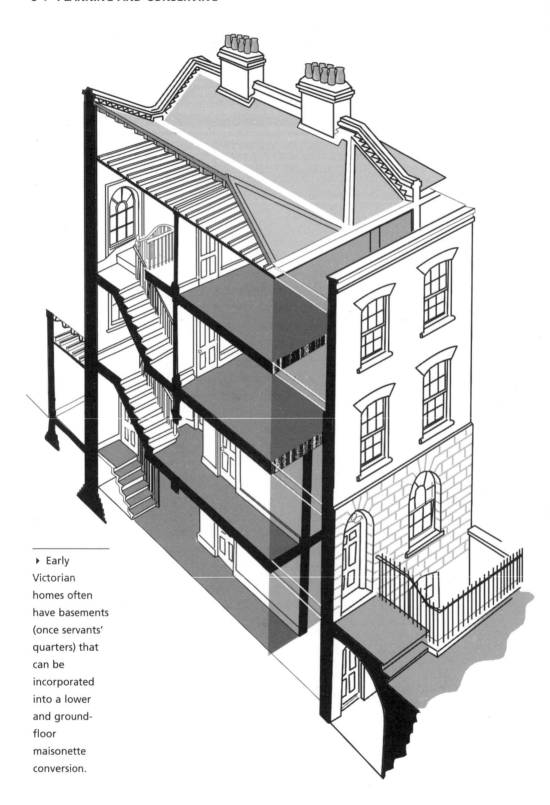

▶ Early Victorian homes often have basements (once servants' quarters) that can be incorporated into a lower and ground-floor maisonette conversion.

Planning permission

Ours is a small island with a growing population, so creating new homes and extra living space without destroying our environment is undeniably one of the biggest challenges facing us. But to achieve it, we have to control it, and those controls begin with the planning system – a filter process through which new homes must pass before they can take their place in the property chain. Aside from the permitted development rights that the creation of an annexe can sometimes fall under, planning permission will be needed, and an understanding of the considerations afforded to your application is essential to a successful one. Alas, the planning system is fiercely democratic, overly bureaucratic and embarrassingly subjective. It is also riddled with unlikely terms, meaningless words and some made-up verbs thrown in for good measure and, I suspect, just to confuse us.

Take the unlikely term 'sustainability'. This was planning jargon not so long ago for 'accessible environments', but now it seems to have been redefined as the buzz word for 'environmentally responsible', or something like it. By the time you read this, it and other words like it will have been bandied about so much (in the knowledge that they will soon be out of fashion) that they will have ceased to mean anything to anybody.

If the government really wanted to streamline the system, it would start by outlawing the jargon. Unfortunately, it seems that the jargon is here to stay and we must therefore deal with it. Hopefully, what follows in this chapter will help to make sense of some of it, cut through the rest and make something pretty out of the red tape that will be left over.

Planning applications

In practice, there are two types of planning permission for which you can apply: full (with plans) and outline (without plans). In 2006, however, the system was overhauled to increase the information needed for outline applications, and for home dividing a full application with plans is essential.

Along with the quality (space and facilities) of the homes, the increase in occupation will need to be assessed and its impact on the amenities, appearance, highway safety and access considered. Some may be fundamental to the 'site', which will be seeing an intensified use when a number of apartments are proposed. On smaller projects, such as annexes, the principle planning interest may be to ensure that it is occupied by family members only. If your building lies within a Conservation Area or within the curtailage of a listed building, design considerations are likely to be at the fore.

Full applications leave nothing to be dealt with later, except what lies within the conditions attached to the permission. Those conditions, which have to be enforceable by the authority, may include details of landscaping or amenity space, but fundamentally the layout of the building is considered in the full application and hence drawings of reasonable detail are required.

Given that most drawings are now prepared on CAD (computer-aided design) software and not actually with pen and paper, most councils now accept applications electronically via the planning portal system. On this, they can also be tracked through the process from the day of submission.

The plans necessary when submitting a full planning application should include:

◆ Scale 1:50 floor layouts and elevations both as existing and as proposed, to indicate the individual uses of rooms and units.
◆ Dated and numbered plans, with the numbers cross-referenced onto the application form.
◆ A site location plan should be included of 1:1250 scale with the plot outlined in red, and any adjoining land that you control outlined in blue. If there are any rights of way nearby you should show them edged in brown. Ordnance Survey extracts are available, usually as print-outs from the digital mapping system, at a charge.
◆ Floor layout plans with internal dimensions and room sizes (floor areas) quoted for each.
◆ Elevations of all sides of the home, illustrating any proposals to facing materials or new windows and doors. If other buildings are close by (adjoining) it may be appropriate to show the new dwelling in context to them and the overall street scene. A clear and well-drawn architectural plan will help because presentation of any proposal enhances it, and the use of colour in elevations is beneficial if it can be accurately reproduced.

Site block plan

In addition to the location plan, a zoom-in on the plot itself must be included and a scale of 1:500 or 1:100 is what is needed, depending on the size of the plot and the plan. This is the drawing that will show the siting of the building and its environment, trees, driveway, parking areas and paths. All boundaries need to be clearly marked, as well as the building's distance from them, and the boundary treatment proposed or existing – such as privet hedging or 1.8-m brick wall – should be included.

Open-plan flat or bedsitter

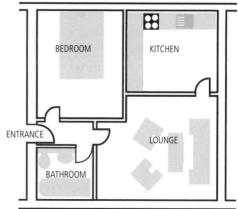

Flat with separate habitable rooms and entrance hall

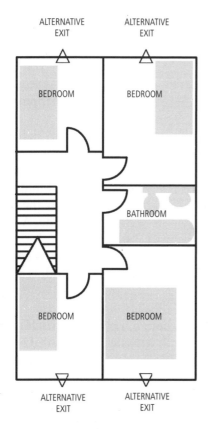

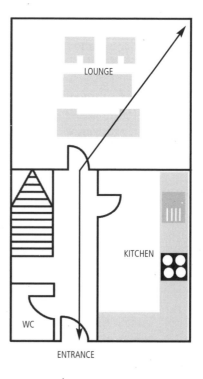

Multi-storey flat with alternative exits (escape windows) from each habitable room, except at entrance level

Existing trees that are affected by the proposals need to be identified, along with their species and crown spread. Later, a survey may have to be undertaken and advice sought on their pruning and removal. Most authorities have a policy that seeks to keep existing trees in place wherever possible, and part of your planning application form will address this very question. If your site lies with the confines of a Conservation Area, it is an offence to lop or fell any trees at all with the express consent of the council, to which you must give at least six weeks' notice.

Submitting your application

In paper form, planning applications have to be made in multiple copies – commonly six sets of plans and six sets of forms (signed twice on each). Local planning authorities have a great deal of consulting to do on applications, and copies are required to be forwarded to consultees and made available for interested parties to view. Online applications are much easier to copy and forward as necessary.

Those who are likely to be consulted on your planning application include:

◆ the local parish and town councils
◆ the Highways Authority
◆ the Environment Agency
◆ the Council for the Protection of Rural England
◆ neighbours (public representations)
◆ conservation officers
◆ tree preservation officers
◆ environmental health officers
◆ county archaeologists
◆ local water authority

Neighbour notification

In England and Wales, the local planning authority will notify your neighbours of your proposals either by letter, advertisement in the local press or by a notice displayed in public nearby. In Scotland, the responsibility to consult with neighbours is yours. Forms for this purpose are usually acquired with the planning application forms and should be returned completed when the application is made. In the former, interested parties have a couple of weeks to lodge their objections, if any.

Many people and organisations are consulted in the planning process – parish councils, environmental groups, etc. Even if there are objections, it does not necessarily mean that your application will be refused. It does usually mean that it will be presented at a planning committee meeting and will thus be decided by councillors rather than through the delegated powers of planning officers.

In Northern Ireland, planning applications are made to the Department of the Environment for Northern Ireland, which has six divisional offices. They carry out the planning function in place of the local authorities, although they do consult with them.

You should receive a letter or e-mail receipt once your application is deposited, together with a date eight weeks in advance which is the statutory date by which the application should be decided. Be warned, though, that decisions that are not made in this period are deemed refused (not approved), and the date can be extended with your consent. In other words, there is no motive in the legislation for applications to be dealt with expediently. To try to make up for this, central government has been offering financial lures in the form of planning development grants to authorities that meet their decision dates. The system remains flawed, however, and delays can still be lengthy.

A programme of the planning committee meeting dates should also be available, and agendas for these can be sought a few days in advance of each meeting. These are public meetings, and you are able to attend and have your say. It should be possible to find out in advance whether your application is recommended for refusal or approval by the planning case officer and what the objections are. If you do decide to attend the meeting, you may need to give notice in advance that you are coming and be aware that you are not usually allowed to question the committee or indeed enter into a debate with them. There may even be a time limit of a few minutes imposed on your speech. As with appeals against planning decisions, restrict your commendation of the proposals to planning issues, but note that the committee may elect to postpone the decision to visit the site, for example.

Things to consider when applying for planning permission

Size

Local authorities have varying policies when it comes to dividing homes into apartments or maisonettes, the first of those considerations often looks at the size of the building to begin with and asks one very important question: is it big enough to divide up?

What passes for 'yes' are minimum values that may vary from one area to the next. As a guideline, it is going to need to cover at least 100 m² in floor area (and for some areas, possibly a lot more) and, as an existing dwelling, it will need at least four bedrooms (and, for some areas, five). The self-contained homes created within will also have minimum floor areas to achieve, depending upon how many bedrooms they themselves will offer.

In their smallest form, some self-contained apartments such as studio flats can seem ultra-compact, but even here there is guidance for minimum sizes. It varies again from place to place, but 30 m² of floor area is often considered the bottom line. In some large family homes 30 m² is the living room, and the garage is likely to be bigger. In the right location, however, even the smallest studio flats offering compact and contemporary living are quite marketable. Modular design techniques can be used to make the space functional within an open-plan arrangement unencumbered by room partitions and doors. Studio flats do not have to accommodate a double bed, but a full-size single has to go somewhere, even when the space may have to be found on a gallery. Indeed, galleried flats are increasingly fashionable and make for a creative use of limited space.

Here are some typical examples of minimum room sizes for one- and two-bedroom apartments and maisonettes used in the Housing Quality Indicators (HQIs) published in the year 2000. The HQIs are guidelines aimed at getting property valued by quality, rather than just price. Housing associations and local authorities use them to try to raise the standard of housing by setting minimum levels of basic quality.

MINIMUM ROOM SIZES FOR ONE- AND TWO-BEDROOM APARTMENTS AND MAISONETTES		
Room	Minimum area (m²)	Minimum width (m)
Lounge	14	3.05
Lounge/kitchen/diner	20	3.05
Kitchen/diner	13	2.13
Master bedroom	11	2.44
Bedroom 2	8	2.13

Taken from Housing Quality Indicators (2000)

The floor areas quoted in housing standards are usually net floor areas measured internally and excluding balconies. They also tend to impose minimum ceiling height dimensions to avoid the sleeping gallery being pinned underneath the ceiling or indeed loft apartments that offer limited opportunity for the residents to stand upright. Spaces with low eaves and sloping ceilings that come too far down can still be viable in terms of living space, however, as these particular areas can be utilised for furniture and beds. To make allowance for this, the ceiling height limit is often set at 1.50 m or thereabouts. That means that floor space is not floor space when the headroom directly over it is less than 1.50 m.

Compared to a studio flat, a one-bedroom apartment will have to provide more space because it is expected that it might provide accommodation for a couple. Now, the bedroom needs space for a double bed, and the minimum total floor area goes up to nearer 40 m². For two-bedroom apartments and maisonettes, you can add another 10, to make a total of 50 m². To limit the size of bathrooms, showers instead of baths can be installed, which will provide more floor space around the appliances. For the most part, minimum floor areas are not used for these rooms. Planning departments tend to concern themselves more with bathroom windows, if they exist (and they do not have to, as these rooms can be internal), and whether they are overlooked by other homes.

In large developments, it makes sense to achieve the perfect balance of quantity and size of units. What is possible in terms of density will be decided at the planning permission stage.

These are, of course, only guidelines. Flexibility or smaller sizes may be acceptable in some areas, but just as importantly you should be looking at dividing the home up to its best potential. That means making the most of daylight, ventilation, privacy, shape and height, as well as finding the most economic use of space. Consideration for the neighbours and minimising the disturbance to them in the conversion will also help you to gain planning permission.

Internal room and daylight

It is unrealistic to assume that all the rooms will have an external wall where a window already exists or can be provided. It rarely happens that way, and some of the rooms will be internal. Rendered windowless, kitchens can be located internally as far as the Building Regulations are concerned – all that is needed are ventilation ducts to draw air in for appliances and extract stale air from cooking. Both planning and environmental health departments can take a different view. They see kitchens as important rooms where not just fresh air but also daylight should be provided, and I agree with them. I have seen plenty of internal kitchens in both new-build apartments and conversions, and they never seem right. The opportunity to throw open a window and let the air be purged in a moment or do the washing up in daylight should be the very least anyone can expect. Those kitchens that do not have the benefit of daylight can still be functional, but they take on the aspect of a large cupboard or store. Internal kitchens tend to happen because the bedrooms and living rooms need those windows even more, and there are only so many outside walls to go around. Daylight can sometimes be introduced, however, through roof windows or sun pipes ducted down from the roof above, and these should be considered where no outside wall exists for a window. Using them exclusively to light more habitable rooms could be a problem unless you can control them for ventilation as well, but they will be far more favourable than no light at all in kitchens and bathrooms.

EcoHomes standard

Introduced by the Building Research Establishment (BRE), the EcoHomes rating procedure is a voluntary scheme to promote more environmentally friendly, or 'greener', homes. It is widely used by housing associations and, if you were thinking of leasing your divided homes to them on completion, it would be a definite asset. Registered consultants would be engaged at the design stage and, using a checklist with items similar to those listed in the following pages, they will assess your proposals and award points. Some of the questions and points attributed to them are a little obscure and hard to explain, but on the whole the system makes sense and has been designed to encourage developers to think about green issues whether they are refurbishing, converting or building homes from new. It is therefore about the design and location of the homes and not about you or the way they will be occupied. An EcoHome rating could be kept in the home information pack alongside the approvals and electrical and heating certificates.

This questionnaire works by subtotalling the points collected through seven sections; these are then weighted and added up at the end to reach a final score. The score is measured as a percentage against the maximum possible score to achieve a rating.

In each of these seven areas, here are some of the issues that will score you points with your design: points that will convert into a better EcoHomes standard.

Energy efficiency

Carbon dioxide emissions
The SAP (standard assessment procedure) ratings that must be awarded to any new home when it comes to carbon dioxide emissions are also used in this process. With improved thermal insulation installed (generally insulation is only used in latitudes

north of 35°N and south of 35°S), comparison should be made to the following U-values (thermal, or heat, transmission values; the higher the value, the more heat is conducted) through each of the following elements of your home:

◆ pitched roofs
◆ flat roofs
◆ external walls
◆ external/ground floor
◆ windows
◆ external doors

These are judged against the national (Building Regulation/code) standard in your country/region. The aim here is to have a lower U-value than the standard. For example, for a roof where the standard is a maximum U-value of 0.20 W/(mK) and you achieve 0.18 W/(mK), you can earn points for your 10 per cent improvement.) A range of U-value improvements from 3 per cent up to 15 per cent (in 3 per cent increments) will score you points proportional to that improvement.

PERCENTAGE BETTER THAN NATIONAL STANDARD	
3 per cent	minimum points
15 per cent	maximum points

Drying space
In terms of energy efficiency, this means either an outdoor washing line or an area indoors in a heated space if a humidistat-controlled extractor fan exists to remove excess humidity.

Rating white goods
Any of the following appliances with energy ratings as shown increase energy efficiency:

◆ fridges/freezers with an A rating
◆ washing machines/dishwashers with an A rating
◆ washer-dryers and dryers with B rating or better (if no A-rated appliance available)
  OR
◆ no white goods

External lights
◆ All general space lighting to be compact fluorescent lamps (CFLs) or fluorescent strip lighting.
◆ All security lighting to be limited to 150 watts maximum and fitted with combined daylight sensor and PIR detector. Any other lights to be compact fluorescent or florescent strip light fittings only, with dawn-to-dusk sensors or timers.
◆ Solar-powered LED lighting utilised.

Transport

Public transport
Good access to public transport is another plus on the environmentally friendly scale, as well as adding convenience. Choose from the following based on your home's location as either rural or urban/suburban.

Urban and suburban areas where you are within either:
a. 500 m (yards) of a 15-minute peak time and 30-minute off-peak time service; or
b. 1000 m (yards) of an hourly service or community bus service

Rural areas where you are within either:
a. 500 m (yards) of an hourly service; or
b. 1000 m (yards) of an hourly service or community bus service.

Cycle storage
This means a sheltered space to secure at least one bicycle (not inside the home).

Home office space

Home office space does not have to be large at all, but there are limits to how small it can be to qualify. I have seen landings at the top of stairs being marketed as home offices simply because there was a plug point there (which I assumed, like everybody else, was for the vacuum cleaner), and clearly this is not acceptable. The minimum criteria are:

◆ at least 1.8 m of wall
◆ a minimum of two double-plug wall sockets
◆ an openable window for ventilation and daylight
◆ two telephone points (one for the phone/fax and one for modem), or one point and broadband Internet facility.

Pollution

Among other things, this relates to your insulation material's Ozone Depletion Potential and Global Warming Potential (available from the insulation manufacturers or suppliers). All insulation in the home must have a zero ODP rating and a GWP rating below 5 to achieve one point.

NOX EMISSIONS FOR PRIMARY HEATING AND HOT-WATER GENERATION	
Solar or heat exchanger geothermal	maximum points
Condensing boilers (gas/oil-fired)	↑
Non-condensing (gas/oil-fired) boilers	
CHP/wood burners (stoves)	↓
Electric heating	minimum points

Reduction of surface rainwater run-off
In periods of heavy rainfall, sewer systems become overcharged and this can cause flooding. Limiting the flow of rainwater into the sewer by using flow attenuation or storage tanks as a stop-off point along the way helps to reduce this. Measures can include:

◆ reducing the flow running off the roof by at least half
◆ reducing the flow running off the drive, patio and pathway by at least half

Zero emission (renewable) energy source
If at least 10 per cent of your heat, hot water or electrical demand is met by renewable sources, such as solar energy, wind, ground-source heat pumps, PV systems, micro-hydro power, you can score one point.

Materials

This relates to the environmental impact of your home's construction materials. (This sub-section is *not* about the insulation U-values, which are contained in the energy-efficiency sub-section (pages 16–18) on the EcoHomes standard; this is about the embodied energy present in the materials themselves.) Minimum points indicates the least-appropriate material to choose, while maximum points indicate the most environmentally friendly.

Roof
Concrete structure . . . . .minimum points
Timber structure . . . . .maximum points

External walls
Concrete . . . . .minimum points
Masonry (brick-faced)
Timber-framed (masonry-faced)
Timber (single leaf –
   render-/tile-/board-faced) . . . . .maximum points

Internal walls
Blockwork, concrete or brickwork . . . . .minimum points
Timber or metal studwork . . . . .maximum points

Floors
Concrete . . . . .minimum points
Timber . . . . .maximum points

Windows and doors
PVC-u frames . . . . .minimum points
Aluminium frames
Timber frames . . . . .maximum points

External surfaces
Concrete . . . . .minimum points
Reclaimed bricks or stone . . . . .maximum points

Boundary protection
Timber fencing . . . . .minimum points
Hedging . . . . .maximum points

Timber

Are the timber products and elements of your home sustainably rated by one of the following schemes?

   FSC (Forest Stewardship Council)
   PEFC (Program for Endorsement of Forestry Certification)
   CSA (Canadian Standards Association)
   MTCC (Malaysian Timber Certification Council)
   SFI (Sustainable Forestry Initiative)

If 50 per cent or more have certification, you score one point.

Recycling

Actual space for storing waste (inside and out) for recycling is what matters here, and a total capacity of 30 litres is the minimum for both.

Internal storage of recycling material . . . . .maximum points
External storage of recycling material . . . . maximum points

If at least 10 per cent of the products and materials in your home
are recycled products and materials . . . . .maximum points

Water

Water use
◆ Metered water usage of:
    No more than 50 m³ per person per year . . .minimum points
    No more than 30 m³ . . . . .maximum points

◆ External water use by rainwater harvesting, with water butts of
  at least 100 litres.

◆ Recycling grey and/or rainwater in WCs and laundry – eg
  harvesting system.

Ecology

Points towards a better EcoHomes rating can be gained when:

◆ You have followed the recommendations of a registered
  ecological consultant in enhancing the environment around
  your home/garden.
◆ You are protecting any ecological features around your home
  identified by a registered ecological consultant, such as trees,
  streams, ponds or hedges.
◆ You have earned by default where no existing features are
  identified.
◆ You have enhanced the ecological value of your home/garden.

Building footprint

This is a value ratio of floor area to footprint where bungalows
and two-storey homes fail, and townhouses succeed.

If your building has more than two storeys (eg two storeys plus
loft conversion or habitable basement), it will score a point.

Health and well-being

Daylight
Daylight is a precious commodity that not only improves our
health, but also reduces our need for artificial lighting. You will
gain one point for meeting each of the following criteria:

◆ Kitchens (15 per cent of floor area in glazed doors or windows)
◆ Habitable rooms (20 per cent of floor area in glazed doors or windows)
◆ Skylights (of any size)

Sound insulation

You need to ensure that excessive or unwanted noise is minimised and that your home meets current (Building Regulation/code) standards in relation to the following:

◆ Are there any party walls or floors separating it from another dwelling?
◆ Are the bathroom and bedroom walls and floors acoustically insulated from adjoining rooms and rooms below?

(Note: this does not apply to bedroom walls separating en-suite bathrooms, dressing rooms or to walls with doors.)

Private Space

You gain one point for each of the following (in this assessment, 'private' does not mean secluded; spaces can be overlooked by neighbours etc):

◆ balcony
◆ private garden
◆ communal garden
◆ roof terrace

You can add the points together if you have a private garden and a balcony, for example, but bear in mind that a balcony has to be set foot on to count – balustrade French doors or Juliet balconies cannot be included.

Working out your final EcoHomes rating

The previous pages should have given you a simplified idea of what is involved in pursuing an eco-rating. You will need to employ a consultant at the design stage of your project. The final calculation process is also more complex than shown in the chart below (given just to show you the principle), and your certified consultant will need to do this calculation for you. The 'weightings' are fixed constants to balance out the points proportionally so that a percentage total can be reached.

ECOHOMES RATINGS TABLE

Rating table

Category	Calculation	Rating subtotal (%)
Energy	points x weighting =	
Transport	points x weighting =	
Pollution	points x weighting =	
Materials	points x weighting =	
Recycling	points x weighting =	
Water	points x weighting =	
Land uses and ecology	points x weighting =	
Health and well-being	points x weighting =	
	FINAL TOTAL =	%

Score table

No. of stars	Rating	Percentage value
*	PASS	36%
**	GOOD	48%
***	VERY GOOD	60%
****	EXCELLENT	70%

If you add up your score and it is below 36 per cent, you need to do a little more eco-friendly converting to your home. Take a look at the areas where you did not score points and see if you can make some improvements.

For example, one-bedroom apartments are not considered to be family homes. As such, they seldom require any garden or amenity space, unless you were aiming for a very good EcoHomes standard. Even then, a balcony will score you a point, so you have to get what you can in this rating system. Where the standard is required by planning policy or your market forces, it is usually set at 'very good' – 60 per cent or more.

Reducing noise by design

Although sound insulation between homes within the same building is covered comprehensively under Building Regulations, it also crops up in planning considerations where it seeks to control disturbances to neighbours. What is known in planning terms as the 'stacking' principle is at the heart of sound insulation. It harks back to the days when the Building Regulations did not propagate such a high standard for cutting out noise by requiring sound testing to be carried out before homes can be occupied. The principle is to have quiet rooms such as bedrooms above other bedrooms on each floor, and noisy rooms such as kitchens above other kitchens. If you have to mix and match, try to position a bedroom over a bathroom, for example, and not a lounge.

The stacking principle is not a bad one to apply. Still, as most developers and home dividers make a point of applying overkill to sound-reduction work to be on the safe side when it comes to sound testing (covered in chapter 3), it is not quite so important any more.

In addition to reducing noise from one part of the building to another, you may also need to reduce external noise from busy roads and railway lines, for example. Windows are the problem with external noise; it can leak around them and vibrate through them. A sealed secondary double-glazed unit fitted to the internal reveals of a window opening will cut down external noise dramatically when varying glass thicknesses are used. Vents that are being installed for background ventilation or for extractor fans can be purchased with sound-reducing baffles. Doors can be draught-sealed to prevent noise as well as air leaking around them. All of these things will have a bearing on reducing noise pollution.

Access

People

Accessibility for people is about inclusive design. Within our communities there live people separated by age across a broad scale and abilities across an even wider range, and making sure that those differences do not exclude them from the built environment is everybody's responsibility. Your divided homes will hopefully be visited and lived in by just a sample of the population, but, in designing them to be accessible for all, that sample will not exclude so many. Building designers have in the past been criticised, and quite justifiably, for creating buildings that only able-bodied males in the 18- to 50-year-old age group can use – all but excluding great swathes of the population from pensioners, children and expectant mums to people with physical and mental disabilities. Heavy doors, steps, thresholds, narrow openings, undersized cloakrooms, low power sockets and high switches have all served as barriers to much of the population in one way or another.

In the homes that you create, albeit from dividing up existing buildings and space, you have the opportunity to make them as accessible as they can possibly be – in other words, user- and visitor-friendly. The following chapter's advice is borne in mind when outlining below the sort of measures that you can take to achieve this.

Bicycles

For the majority of divided homes, garden space is in short supply. A little is all you need, however, for a cycle store. Traditionally, the bicycle has always had to be dragged into the common hallway of a block of flats and left leaning against the wall for somebody to fall over. Cycle spaces outside your home that are secure and sheltered are becoming increasingly attractive to tenants and owners alike.

We have not been building bike shelters around homes, but I am sure they would be well received if we did. A low lean-to roof structure to form a miniature carport with a wall anchoring point for the lock is all that is needed, and with some thought the design materials could blend with the building and complement it. A single bicycle can be housed in a store with internal dimensions of just 2 m by 1m. All it needs is enough wall cover to keep it dry and an anchor point provided so that it can be chained securely.

Bins

Storage for bins is required by legislation. Planning and Building Regulations look for minimum space for solid waste to be stored in and collected from. The space required is simply that, space, and it is not that great either. Given that nobody likes to see dustbins rolling in the road or rubbish spilled over their garden, however, a bin store is the best way to achieve it. Now that we have joined the recycling race to sort our waste into separate boxes and bins, we need more room for it anyway.

From a hygiene aspect, enclosed bin stores outside of the homes are ideal, as they keep rats, foxes and domestic cats from using it as a takeaway.

If you are building a cycle store, carport or garage, a bin store hiving off and semi-detached from it would be perfect. As local authorities push harder to engage us in reducing our waste and recycling what we can, an organised storage point for your divided homes will be a useful feature – particularly if the day comes when charging for waste removal by volume is widely introduced, as it is in the Republic of Ireland. Securely locked bins or bin stores become necessary to prevent waste being 'transferred' between neighbours.

Cars and parking

If no off-street parking is proposed, the effects on the highway have to be considered, but in a central urban area with good transport links that should not be an issue now. Flexibility has appeared in the planning system when it comes to car parking.

Not so very long ago, the scale of a development translated directly to the number of parking spaces it needed. Planners were demanding minimum numbers of spaces. And, in a cart-driving-the-mule kind of way, it unwittingly promoted car ownership and use. Cars, rather than people, have determined the design of our built environment, and our dependency on them has grown and grown.

Trying to reverse this trend may not be easy, but that is exactly what is being attempted now. Today, maximum numbers are applied, not minimums, and space for cars is being capped to a limit for each new home. Of course, car ownership has not reduced – not yet, anyway – and I can think of many new housing developments where parking spaces have been kept to a minimum and, now the developments are occupied, the streets around them are congested with cars parked at all angles on road and pathways alike. Doing away with the car will not be so easy, and usually some parking space is needed when homes are divided and the occupancy of a building is being increased. In 2007, the government appears to have removed its previous advice to local authorities for a maximum 1.5 spaces per dwelling, and now leaves the matter to 'design' and the regional and local design guides of planning authorities. If you are wondering for what type of car half a space serves (so am I,) it appears to be for visitors who presumably cannot all turn up at once. If you are dividing a home into two, three spaces for both dwellings together may be acceptable. You might be able to convince your planning authority that extra spaces are needed if you live in a rural or suburban area with poor links to public transport, but your chances of succeeding may not be good in an urban location. If you feel that you require more parking spaces than your council will usually allow, it will be a case of having to demonstrate that they are necessary.

So, car parking may be an issue in suburban or rural locations, but not so much so in town centres where amenities and public transport are within walking range. Your local planning authority should have a published design guide with policies that illustrate what they expect to see in the way of off-street parking per unit. Although these figures may have been watered down in recent years, they still can determine the density of occupation.

Driveways are fine in themselves, but front-garden parking is becoming less desirable to planning authorities. They have seen what a road full of small front-garden car parks looks like by now, and it is not pretty. Armed with the word 'streetscape', which they have written into local plans and policies, they try to get cars not just off the road, but off the front garden as well.

They do have a point when front gardens are small. Having them entirely occupied by an SUV is not attractive. Nobody likes to see the streets cluttered with parked cars, but we have reached a point where our front gardens are now adorned with them. Our track record in the United Kingdom for front garden design has never been brilliant, and a plethora of SUVs certainly does not improve it. If, on the other hand, the front garden is large enough that it can be landscaped as well as allowed to provide parking, then fine. If it is not, then look to the back and side of the building (if they exist) first.

If you have garden space to spare, you could do worse than provide some garaging. It would be made to feel much more welcome than a driveway alone. Garaging is still provided for by many new home builders, but it is often woefully undersized. To make matters worse, the scale of our cars has increased over the past 20 years. Tall and wide SUVs and MPVs are popular modes of transport today, and they do not fit inside British garages. Our garage spaces were never big enough unless you owned a Mini, but now they are hopelessly inadequate. Along with cars, our other storage requirements have increased, needing to take account of a variety of garden machines from mowers to shredders and leaf blowers, all needing to be kept alongside patio tables and sun loungers. Not surprisingly, our garages are not up to it.

You really do need the garden space to make it worthwhile. Even communal garages are not a good idea unless you can make them a good size; build a carport instead. A garage that was 2.4 m wide by 5.5 m long was the British standard, but this size is next to useless now. If you make it 6 m long by 4 m wide, you might just be able to open the car door when you are in there to get in and out of it. If you struggle with these dimensions, an open-sided carport (at least open on two sides) will screen the car and avoid the cramped restrictions of four walls. Design-wise, carports can be elegant structures – they do not have to comprise of metal poles supporting corrugated roof sheets. Think traditional with tiled or slated pitch roofs open over brick piers. Above all, try to complement the surrounding architecture.

▲ Keep service pipes and vents to rear elevations where possible.

▼ Low and medium shrubs are better close to the building.

Landscaping

There is always the risk that a home-dividing project will look like an over-intensive use of a property. With parking and bin stores, perhaps additional windows on the front elevation, it can all start to look a bit intense. Landscaping and the treatment of the site boundaries are critical to softening the impact home division will have. Shrubs and hedges can be planted to screen the bin stores or the parking bays, and give some privacy to the main entrance. Landscaping front gardens in the twenty-first century should not be exclusively about gravel and islands of low-growing

shrubs that will not scratch your hubcaps. The low-growing range can be placed at the front on the back edge of kerb, but you can raise the height to medium-sized shrubs in a terraced border, as you step back towards the building.

A landscaping scheme can often be required by condition of planning permission, but submitting one with the scheme in any case can improve the chances of getting permission in the first place. It does, however, need to be thought out and not overdone.

Trees, if they exist, should in most cases be retained; however, if they are large, crowning near windows can block light and be a nuisance to residents. If you have large trees on the site, try to place bathrooms or stairways closest to them, rather than lounge or bedroom windows. If the residents believe the tree is detracting from their enjoyment of the home, they will want it cut down.

Trees can be a pleasure to live with – they create shade in summer from the heat, introduce wildlife to the area, shelter the building from adverse weather, filter pollution from the air and generally exude a feeling of well-being.

▾ High trees shouldn't be allowed to block windows.

Low-growing shrubs	Medium-growing shrubs
◆ Cistus	◆ Aucuba
◆ Clethera	◆ Buddleia
◆ Cotoneaster	◆ Berberis (dwarf varieties)
◆ Cytisus	◆ Hebe
◆ Helianthemum	◆ Mahonia
◆ Hypericum	◆ Pieris
◆ Potentilla	◆ Wiegela
◆ Vinca	

Design statements

You may be required to submit a design statement with your planning application. In written form, these statements lay your plan out and provide a summary of your proposals and the considerations you have made part of it.

Although the 'development' of an existing dwelling by extending it does not require a design statement, creating additional dwellings by dividing it does. Basically that means, if you are extending your home to create an annexe, you will not need a statement unless it happens to be in a Conservation or other designated area such as a national park, Area of Outstanding Natural Beauty, Site of Special Scientific Interest, etc. Your local planning authority should be able to confirm whether you are in one of those areas requiring a statement.

There are six elements to the content of design statements, plus access – which is best done as a separate statement – according to the Town and Country Planning (General Development Procedure) (Amendment) (no.2) (England) Order 2005).

1. Proposed Use

A fairly brief description of the use should head up your design statement, but be very specific about the use – e.g. the conversion of a five-bed single-family dwelling into one two-bedroom self-contained maisonette and one one-bedroom self-contained flat, creating two separate dwellings.

2. Quantum

This is a posh way of saying 'how many' units (homes) are proposed. As well as spelling out in the statement that your proposal is for 'x' number of self-contained dwellings, you should also mark on the plans the unit numbers. Ground-floor plans need clear marking with plot (unit) numbers. When the development is complete, these can be converted into postal addresses on the application for street numbering without too much confusion.

3. Layout

Although your plans should illustrate the layout clearly, the statement should also describe it in words. The approach to the building, its position, the routes to access and egress, the open spaces and the relationship to other buildings and spaces outside of the development should be covered.

4. Scale

With pure conversions where there is no increase in the physical size of the building, this part of the design statement has no relevance. Where they also involve the extension of the building or the construction of a detached annexe, it does. The height, width and length of the proposed new build should be stated, along with the resulting increase in the cubic volume of the building. You may also want to state this increase as a percentage in context with the scale of the existing building, to illustrate statistically the size of the development.

5. Appearance

Appearance means more than a simple description of the materials used externally. It should also cover those aspects of the building which determine the impression it makes. Again, with conversions, appearance may be unaffected by the proposal, but quite often new windows and doors may be necessary, and these will have a bearing. Sometimes, one aspect of a building can be improved by cladding treatments that break up large expanses of one material such as brickwork – a single panel of vertical hanging tiles or timber boards, for example.

In the case of new extensions or hard surfacing (e.g. for car parking and access), landscaping may be an essential part of the scheme and also considered in with appearance.

6. Response to context

This might best be described as a reference to those policies that surround your proposal. The local planning policies and national guidance notes which will be used in judging your application are available (on the Internet, but also in libraries and local council offices). Together with its context in physical, social and economic terms, they will determine whether it is given permission or not.

Access statements

What used to be described as 'access for the disabled', then 'access for people with disabilities', has now finally being referred to as just plain but politically correct 'access'. Applicable to the same home proposals as design statements, access today is about inclusive design for people, and it should be approached in that vein. Instead of making special features for access that are separate and unique, look for an all-inclusive design approach. In this, minority groups such as children, senior citizens and people with disabilities will all be able to get into and use your new homes, just as easily as able-bodied adults.

Access statements are typically needed where there is a significant increase in the number of dwellings on the site and should cover five principles that set out:

1. how the occupiers and visitors will be able to access the homes from the existing transport network and what the access routes and points to the site are;
2. whether any consultation has taken place with local access groups or other bodies, and what, if any, aspects of the outcome of that consultation have been included in the proposal;
3 an explanation of the policy and approach adopted to access, and how the policies relating to access on relevant developments have been taken into account in the design;
4. how any specific issues which might restrict access to the proposals have been addressed; and
5. how in future the access features to the homes will be maintained.

Thermal insulation

Not so long ago, simply dividing a home into two or more would not have attracted much in the way of Building Regulations. All that has changed now: along with fire safety and sound insulation comes thermal insulation.

You may be under the impression that, as the walls, floor and roof already exist and you were not going to rebuild them, you did not have to concern yourself with their thermal insulation qualities. Since 2006, however, that is not the case.

Dividing up a home is a change of use that invokes the requirement for energy efficiency and insulation not just for newly constructed elements, but also for renovated and retained elements. Only a quarter (25 per cent of the area) of an element has to be renovated to qualify for upgrading. In the case of new and renovated elements, what insulation level they have at present is immaterial; they must be reinsulated to the current standard. The situation when it comes to retained elements that you were not going to touch differs slightly. For them, you must assess what value your thermal elements already have. That means carrying out some investigation and determining U-values for them – if they fall below specified threshold levels, you must upgrade them to a higher standard.

Upgrading

◆ Cavity-wall properties built before the early 1980s tend to have no insulation in the cavity and can easily be upgraded by injecting blown-fibre insulation. I have recently raised U-value of the external walls in my 1984 home from an as-built 0.59 W/(mK) to 0.32 W/(mK) by this method. The entire process was carried out externally in only half a day.

◆ Solid walls are a bit harder to improve, and quite often they have a U-value that is well below the threshold currently considered acceptable under the Building Regulations. The only the way they can be upgraded internally is with a system of insulation and plasterboard dry lining.

◆ Floors are easily insulated when they are suspended timber. With the floorboards taken up, insulation can be installed between them and the boards replaced. With concrete floors, the only solution may be to overlay them with insulation and new boarding as a floating finish or fixed to battens, but that of course raises the level of the floor and brings all that that entails into play.

◆ Loft spaces are easily and economically upgraded, but the depth of insulation can make them less acceptable afterwards. A 'room in the roof' scenario with sloping ceilings can be treated like a loft conversion, but with the unwelcome complication of having to remove the plasterboard ceilings, to carry out the insulation work, and replacing them afterwards.

All of these are internal works and designed to force home owners into reducing carbon emissions from the existing housing stock. Of course, insulation improvements can also be made on the outside of the building if need be. A roof that is being stripped of its covering for new tiles can be insulated before the tiles are relaid. A wall that is being covered by cladding can be lined with insulation first.

For retained elements, insulation is an additional expense that you may not have previously considered, and you may feel that you can justify not carrying out some of the upgrade work needed in this respect. There is a mechanism for objecting if the works seem unreasonable; however, as with everything else, it is highly complex.

What is reasonable has to be measured in three ways: technically feasible, functionally feasible and economically feasible. All of these wonderful alliterations mean complicated assessments.

'Technically feasible' speaks for itself. The work to be carried out has to be recognised as physically achievable and known as an approved method using approved materials. If it can be physically achieved as it should without adversely affecting the property, it is technically reasonable.

'Functionally feasible' is similar, but not quite the same thing – it needs to work and achieve the insulation that it sets out to provide.

'Economically feasible' is everybody's favourite because it says how much the work will cost and decides, even when the work is technically and functionally feasible, whether it is worthwhile or not. Worthwhile means that it has to have paid for itself in savings within 15 years. This is known as the 'payback period', and it is the time span allowed to recover the cost of doing the upgrade. Fifteen years is usually non-negotiable.

Working out the savings achieved by insulating is fairly complex. The first thing to establish is the difference between the U-values for the improved elements and multiply these out by the areas of those elements to establish the heat lost from the dwelling as a whole. Within the prescribed energy calculations are published figures for the cost of fuel.

You will need to run a cost comparison for heating your home with and without the upgrade work to see what the benefit of it will be in terms of saved energy cost. This is then compared to the actual cost of the work (excluding VAT). Approved calculation models are available on PC software – they are SAP 2005 (standard assessment procedure) and SBEM (simplified building energy model).

Conserving and restoring

Listed buildings

When buildings are listed on the statutory schedule of listed buildings, a separate application and consent to your planning and Building Regulation ones is required and may well be the most onerous of them all. On a positive note, the application itself is free, and much of the work itself is zero-rated for VAT purposes – but that is where the good news ends. The design statement that will accompany your application will have to show that you have taken account of the historic and architectural importance of the building, recognised and preserved the particular features that have led to it being listed and considered the setting in which it exists.

For buildings that are listed or located in Conservation Areas, dividing them up without losing their character can be a challenge, but is all the more rewarding for it. There is great potential to destroy whatever special features the building has, whether inside or out, and this is precisely what needs to be avoided.

In these conservation projects, a lot more thought has to be given to each element of the work. Features such as windows and doors may need to be retained and renovated, rather than replaced. Pipework for gas, electricity and drainage may need to be raised through the building internally in centralised service shafts, rather than running through the structure wherever they are needed. Vent openings may need to be combined or positioned on the roof to reduce the number of holes appearing on outside walls. Of the most common problems encountered by home dividers in conservation country, it is details such as this that are often overlooked and likely to cause problems.

Preserving doors

It is rarely a problem to renovate an existing front door, and most people would agree that a big old period door, freshly painted and restored to former glory, is an asset. It is quite unusual to find an original door so badly damaged that it has to be replaced. When this does happen, it will be a case of using an empathetic purpose-made door built by a joinery company, rather than fitting an off-the-shelf replacement. This is essentially for one reason: we tend to make doors for the new home market at only 838 mm wide today. In grander Victorian or Edwardian days, the front door was more of a statement, and usually a three-foot wide one. There are, of course, architectural salvage outlets, and you may be lucky enough to find a design and a size that fits before you visit a joiner. Having a drawing or photograph of what is required before you go shopping is essential. Quite often, conservation officers in local authorities will want to see detailed plans drawn to a large scale (e.g. 1:10 section details or 1:20 elevations) of any replacement door or window before it is made and fitted. Joinery details that show cross-sections as well as elevations are important because it is not just the appearance that matters to them. They also need to know that the materials and the construction detail are appropriate for the building.

Multiple external letter boxes (the type that you see on apartment buildings) can be a problem on conservation projects. A single external letter box is often preferred and, consequently, if the main entrance is common to more than one apartment, internal letter boxes may need to be installed in the hallway. Letterboxes in nineteenth-century doors were much smaller than they are today (and hence wholly unsuitable for use today). If your door does have one that needs to be retained as an original feature, it might be best to have it secured shut, and internal boxes provided.

As it is external, the only ironmongery needed to meet modern standards is the lock. A simple deadlock that can be released by a thumb-turn latch is ideal for letting people out of the building instantly in an emergency. Mortice locks that have them searching

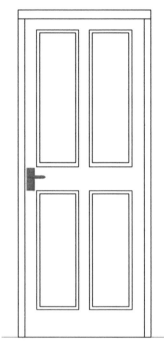

▲ Retaining period door faces in communal areas is often necessary.

for a key are not acceptable on fire-escape routes. It is the internal doors that form the entrances to each apartment that are required to be fire-resistant, and these are often on the front line in the battle between Building Regulations and conservation. Here, entrance doors residing in common stair and hallways need to be FD30s rated. To find a door that is guaranteed for a half-hour fire performance means not only buying it new from a door manufacturer, but also fitting it with smoke seals, door closures and other pieces of approved ironmongery. If the original doors must be retained, upgrading them with suitable materials may be your only option because, in period buildings, doors are often inadequate for fire-resistance. The styles and rails may be made from reasonably thick wood, but the panels are often woefully thin. So much so that when restorers have had them dipped in acid baths to remove the ancient paintwork they have found the door to be embarrassingly insubstantial. The glued joints that were holding it together may have been attacked by the acid, too, and weakened. Gaps between panels, styles and

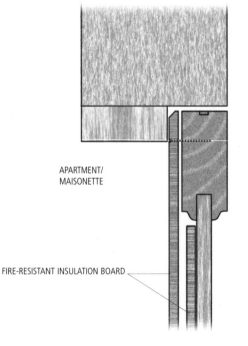

APARTMENT/
MAISONETTE

COMMUNAL HALLWAY

FIRE-RESISTANT INSULATION BOARD

▶ A cross-section of an internal entrance door, with added fire resistant measures.

rails may have been filled by years of repeated painting. Now revealed, the door as a whole may be looking somewhat inadequate – not to mention dried out and even distorted. Everything that a fire door should not look like.

Without question the easiest and best solution in fire safety terms would be to replace the door with a manufactured fire door, but in conservation terms that could be heresy. The door may have to stay and be upgraded on one face. It may be acceptable to simply work on the apartment side of the door and beef up this inner face with known fire-resistant materials such as cement fibreboard, leaving the outer face in its original and conserved form for those approaching the apartment to appreciate. In fire terms, working on the inside face makes sense because it is the stair or hallway that you are trying to protect from a fire within the apartment, and not vice versa. The apartment is the risk, and hence the inner face of the door is the risk face that benefits from being upgraded. Doors can be upgraded (see diagram on page 36), but these measures are not always acceptable to everybody, so be sure to have your proposals approved before you adopt them. I have to admit upgrading doors by thickening them, even after they have been decorated, does not always look very nice. You may prefer to use an intumescent sealant and paint finish to give them the fire-resistance they need.

Intumescent paint
Intumescent paints are essentially chemical formula paints that react to intense heat and expand to encase their host within a fireproof encrustation. Having been activated once, it becomes skip material and hence is not, by any stretch of the imagination, a sustainable material. Its formula contains chemicals that are somewhat unpleasant to be around, and the painter applying it needs to work in an extremely well ventilated space and wear protective clothing. A gauge for measuring the thickness of the coating is usually provided with the tin, so you can check that you have applied the correct amount. Also, as intumescent paint is not recognisable until you apply intense heat to it, a certificate of purchase comes with it. One of the selling points for these paint products is that the finished article appears no different for having been treated – it looks the same as any other paint.

Windows – replace or renovate?

Windows are often a bone of contention between the developer and the conservation officer. We have become accustomed to the plastic window in the belief that it will be maintenance-free and that, once installed, it will never have to be painted, repaired or replaced. Only one of these is true; the others belong to a marketing myth. Plastic windows are not maintenance-free – you just do not have to paint them. In truth, they are onerous to maintain. Hinges break, seals go in the glass and the cost of maintaining them is high if you can find parts that fit. Notoriously difficult are the hinges, which are all different and continuously evolving. Combine this with the fact that plastic window companies want only to sell new windows, not to fix old ones, and you can see how unsustainable they are.

This is an industry that has, since its early days circa 1980, repeatedly reduced the quality of its workmanship and product to a base level, then dipped slightly below it. Plastic windows can be very cheap now, if you do not mind buying a unit that has a dodgy handle to start with, hinges that will break in ten years, glass seals that will leak in five and a quality of fitting that looks like burglary in reverse. Some companies use cheap unqualified labour, with fitters that change as frequently as the weather and salesmen that miraculously jump from quotes of £16,000, down to £6,000, then down to £4,000 to clinch the deal. The business has been seen as a circus of clowns that is only funny to those in the audience and not in the ring. If I am giving you the impression that all replacement windows are bad, I should add that I am referring to only about 95 per cent. There are, at the top end, quality products fitted very well, but they are in the minority and so many people have mistaken a self-certification system (FENSA) as a quality mark rather than an administrative convenience.

When the government brought replacement windows under some control with the Building Regulations, it could not swamp local authorities with the millions of installations that occur, so it introduced a system whereby the industry could certify its own work – a self-certification scheme. Not surprisingly, it has not really changed anything, except that the builders and odd-job men who were fitting a few windows each year for their customers now have to make an application for Building Regulation approval because it is not worth them joining FENSA. As it turns out, their workmanship is usually far superior to the companies who specialise in it regionally. If you have to have your windows replaced with PVC-u as part of the project, my advice is to avoid the large firms, save yourself from the sales patter and go with one of the infrequent installers. At least that way their work will be inspected and approved at the end of the day.

In Conservation Areas and on listed buildings, plastic is considered heresy. It is the exact opposite of conservation, and

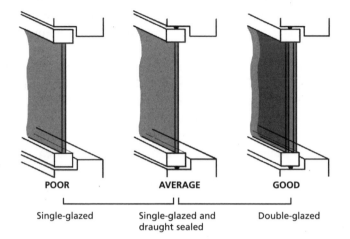

POOR	AVERAGE	GOOD
Single-glazed	Single-glazed and draught sealed	Double-glazed

▲ The scale of sound and heat insulation achieved by windows.

you are unlikely to make a friend of your conservation officer by suggesting that you think they will look great. Unfortunately a dilemma occurs with replacement windows in these situations because the general public and indeed the Building Regulations require you to install double-glazing with a high standard of thermal insulation. Even in timber windows, double-glazing looks, well, like double-glazing, and not at all in keeping with the style of a period building. A contemporary double-glazed pane is likely to have 20 mm of argon gas–filled space between the sheets of glass, making it 28 mm thick overall. A single Victorian pane, by contrast, is likely to be 4 mm thick and allow a rate of heat loss through it that is three times that of the modern window. And so, even double-glazing in timber windows can generate problems. I have seen people try to compromise with mixed success, but clearly some middle ground needs to be found.

Secondary glazing may help, as it leaves the external appearance of the window alone and preserves its architectural character. Internally and set some distance inside the window, a sliding double-glazed unit may be installed with a smaller overall thickness of perhaps 14 mm, comprising of two 4-mm panes and a 6-mm cavity. A secondary double-glazed unit such as this could achieve a U-value of about 3.3 w/(mK) and find itself somewhere between single and contemporary double glazing in terms of thermal performance. Of course, the original window will improve upon that, and hopefully you will be able to keep your release of carbon down along with your heating bill. Secondary glazing in this way is also good for sound insulation and will keep out traffic noise wonderfully.

I know it brings back memories of the 1970s when wallpaper adhesive companies were trying to sell us DIY 'secondary double' glazing that seemed to involve cling film and sticky-back plastic, but things have improved a little since then. The secondary frame needs to be purpose-made as simply as possible and with sufficient rebates to hold the casements or sashes, but nothing larger than the existing. The idea here is to avoid altering the external appearance of the window, and you do not want to see a chunky frame inside reducing the glazed area. As a result, secondary glazing systems have usually been designed in aluminium frames that provide the strength without the size. Aluminium does not do much for the interior design of a period home, however, and my advice is to work with hardwood if you can.

It might be worth asking whether you can replace or re-glaze with a 'slim' 14-mm unit, but it will depend on the appearance as to whether it is successful or not. A dummy unit may have to be submitted as a sample first. If your windows have glazing bars dividing up the window into panes, then the double-glazing world's solution to this is to stick 'mock' bars on the outside of the glass. They do this because the bars would need to be too big and chunky to support double-glazing and the panes are too small to be made economically. If you have ever walked past a modern home where the plastic windows have been fetchingly adorned with dummy glazing bars you will know how this looks. It is not any better with wood. Dummy glazing bars might look authentic when viewed square-on from 30 paces, but at any oblique angle they look as if somebody has super-glued bits of wood or plastic to the outside of your glass, which is exactly what they have done.

Restoring windows

It is not only planners and conservationist who like to retain original windows. For many tenants and home owners alike, the windows are one architectural feature that they would not want to lose. PVC-u windows usually have a disastrous effect on the appearance of a period home, with their chunky smooth featureless frames, and thick panes of glass and replacement timber windows made to measure by joiners are often prohibitively expensive. This leaves you with only one choice: to restore and repair what exists at present and, if you have to upgrade thermally, to secondary double-glaze.

With listed buildings, you have the opportunity of a relaxed standard from the Building Regulations which may allow you to keep the original windows alone, and simply renovate them. Draught-sealing is an essential part of window and door

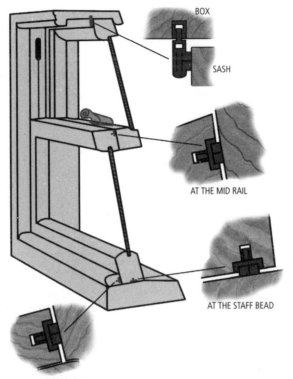

BOX

SASH

AT THE MID RAIL

AT THE STAFF BEAD

AT THE BOTTOM RAIL

◀ Renovating sash windows to exclude noise and draughts.

restoration. Having a 4-mm gap around a badly fitting door is like having a brick missing in your wall. You might not notice it until a cold wind arrives, but then it will seem impossible to keep the room warm. The same applies to windows. Draught-sealing them and making sure the sashes and casements close tightly are half the battle.

Before you look at the openable parts of the window, check over the frame itself and see how well it fits into the wall opening. If over the years it has shrunk away or the wall has deteriorated around it, air may be leaking past the window jambs. A sealing of silicone mastic is the usual solution, but take the time to get the bead width right and use coloured mastic if white is inappropriate. Dark brown is available and ideal against tile hanging and dark brickwork. The silicone mastics remain flexible, so they are long-lasting and far superior to the oil- and resin-based caulking that was once used for this task.

Weather strips

Sash windows

Also known as double-hung windows, sash windows consist of upper and lower vertically sliding parts. They were the standard window of the nineteenth century and at least the first quarter of the twentieth. Each sash is provided with balances on sash cords located within the box-framed jambs. Often these cords need replacing and the operation overhauling to restore the balance and smoothness of the window opening.

Old sash windows are draughty and can even rattle in the wind, leaking heat and bringing in noise as well as cold air. A new apartment left with the original unsealed windows is likely to experience at least three complete air changes per hour. Well-fitted draught stripping can reduce that to around 0.7 air changes per hour. If they alone are to be retained, draught sealing them is essential.

As the sashes run up and down in channels on the jambs, they cannot be so easily draught-proofed without increasing the friction and impairing their opening. It is, however, possible to improve the airtightness of these windows and still retain their appearance and ease of operation. Brush-type weather seals made of durable polypropylene yarn can be fitted into routed-out channels in the frame as a rebated unit. In some cases, it might be possible to fit these seals by removing the existing staff bead and replacing it with one fitted with a proprietary pile draught excluder.

Reglazing these windows because of corner cracks in the pane is commonplace. Remember that anything below 800 mm of floor will need to be reglazed with toughened safety glass and not just the ordinary float glass that it had before. As toughened glass is available in varying thicknesses, it can usually be accommodated in the existing joinery without looking different.

Part of the upgrading of sash windows in conversions can be fitting child-safety locks or window-limiters to the bottom sash. In

▸ Using a high-performance weather seal meets all the requirements of BS 7386:1990.

UNCOMPRESSED 4.5MM WEATHERFIN

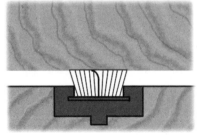

WEATHERFIN COMPRESSED TO 4.5MM

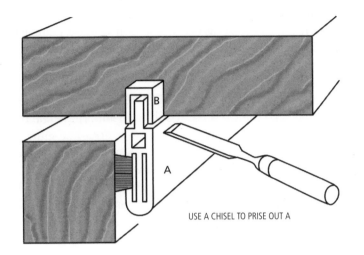

USE A CHISEL TO PRISE OUT A

◄ The parting bead is comprised of the pipe carrier A and its holder B.

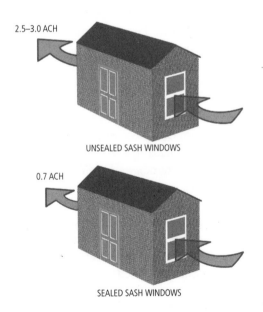

2.5–3.0 ACH

UNSEALED SASH WINDOWS

0.7 ACH

SEALED SASH WINDOWS

◄ A building with sash windows in an exposed position will probably have 2.5–3 air changes per hour (ACH).

Victorian homes, the windowsills on upper floors can be very low to the floor, and anything below 800 mm is a child-safety problem. A restrictor that prevents the bottom sash from being raised too high without it being released can be fitted.

Doors

For doors, the most effective weather strips can be the gasket type that have replaced the cushion or spring metal types. The gaskets today are made of a durable Neoprene that does not split, wear or perish. Neither is it easy to distort these seals and render them ineffective as you might have done with rubber or spring metal strips. They are screwed into the surface of the frame with the Neoprene gasket pushed against the edge of the door, sealing the gap and preventing draughts. You need to offer as much friction as is needed to keep draughts at bay, but not so much as to make the door hard to open.

If a gap exists between the bottom of the door and the sill, a draught here will be the most damaging of all and capable of bringing with it rain that has run off the door face and blown beneath. With new doors (now designed without water bars and thresholds that prevent wheelchair access), draught-sealing the bottom edge has become more critical than ever before. Shallow and rounded aluminium thresholds fitted to the sill are all that the weather stripping fitted to the underside of the door has to locate against in most arrangements. The tolerances are not great and, while these are fine for new doors, you will find that the door's weather stripping will not close a large discrepancy in an old door. The brush-type seals that stand up proud but are resilient enough to be walked over are the best option here, but you must look for those designed for wheelchair access, as they will stand up to robust use. It is worth fitting a rain strip to any external door that lacks a metal water bar. Pinned to the outside of the door near the base, the strip fits with the bottom edge flush to the door's underside and deflects the rain away from this vulnerable area.

A door shoe-style fitting that contains both draught excluder and rain strip in one aluminium extrusion is often ideal, but again it depends on the size of the gap. Typically these shoes have a set of fingers over a bubble-shaped Neoprene gasket that push over the threshold once the door is closed. They will take a small degree of intolerance in the gap, but not a huge amount.

Pods

There is a tendency with flat conversions for grand homes to be made into small inconsequential homes – pods within a building.

While this does not matter so much in ordinary situations, in a listed building it is often disastrous. Imagine a ten-foot ceiling framed with a deep and decorative plaster cornice and a foot-high skirting board rudely interrupted by a studwork-and-plasterboard wall every few metres, dividing it into boxes of accommodation.

If you do have a listed building of some scale and grandeur, you may need to restrict the flats to one per floor and avoid as much as you can the subdivision of the existing rooms. I know this is a tough choice, but period features are very marketable. You need to think long and hard before you lose them. Creating bathrooms and kitchens in what may be only two large rooms, one front and one back, does not have to mean building boxes in the corners of rooms. Clearly these wet rooms will need to connect to the drainage system and that will usually determine the side of the house on which they are located. From therein, it may be a case of trying to minimise their impact. Where you can, look towards a layout that involves the least disruption to the fabric of the building. Open-plan room layouts might be more suitable. Kitchen/lounge/dining rooms that flow through one large room space, with the kitchen located farthest from the entry doorway and the dining space adjacent to the kitchen and also as a buffer to the lounge area may work.

A single-bedroom apartment can have the luxury of a single en-suite shower room, but two bedrooms creates a common bathroom need. Although every once in a while I meet somebody who is happy to install en-suite facilities within a bedroom (open plan, as it were), most of us expect the privacy of a wall to separate them. If it is just a shower or a bath, a simple screen is often sufficient. Glass blocks or crazed laminate panels that reach 2 m, but not the ceiling, make ideal screens that still allow light to flow through the apartment without creating solid divisions. If it is possible to separate the WC out to its own location, do not be afraid to do it. In many European countries, the idea of having the toilet in the same room as the bath or shower is abhorrent. WCs with small hand basins in attendance do not take up much space, and you might be able to locate them in an unused cupboard or under-stair space out of the way. Avoid putting them near kitchens. Although it is not a problem as far as the Building Regulations are concerned, most people like a ventilated space between a WC and a kitchen. We went through a spell in the 1960s and 1970s when this was required under public health acts. It was a time when many of our Victorian homes with back addition kitchens but no indoor WCs were being modernised, with bathrooms built off the kitchen as a back addition. This was usually achieved by placing a small lobby and a back door between the two. It worked perfectly well, but the only problem with those homes today is the fact that often that back addition had walls of single brick and those bathrooms tend to be too cold in winter. If you are working to divide a home from this arrangement, you will need some advice on insulating.

Timber treatment and repair

A point I feel inclined to make is this: the Victorians were not all quality builders. They had cowboys, too. Much of their housing was the product of low-grade labour with mass-produced materials, and some of their building practices have today left us with problems. Timbers were often built into solid brick walls, either as plates to sit floor joists on or as joist and beam bearings. After a century of damp penetration, not surprisingly they can be rotten.

I regularly visit a road of large Victorian homes that were once guesthouses which are being converted to apartments, and although they vary a little they all have suffered some timber rot. The damp and decay are usually extreme around the bay windows and at joist ends on the exposed elevations, and these timbers have very little substance left in them. Be prepared to expose some nasty surprises when you hack off lathe and plaster ceilings. When timbers are badly affected like this, they must be removed entirely, or partially at the very least, with a new 'cripple' supporting timber fixed to replace the removed section.

Insect and fungal attack can be treated, but it depends on the type and severity as to how you treat it, and consequently you cannot embark on a particular solution until you know exactly what problems you face. White rot is an illustrative description of wet rot, as it has the effect of making the wood paler. It also cracks along the grain, but not across it. Brown rot is so called because it darkens the wood, and the wood will crack in both directions, along and across the grain. Brown rot could, in very dry and extreme cases, cause the timber to crumble and ultimately turn to dust.

With any form of fungal attack, dampness is at the heart of the cause. It may be directly penetrating from a leaking roof, porous wall or broken drainpipe, or it could be caused by condensation from a lack of ventilation through the voids of the building, but it still amounts to dampness. What's more, removing the cause is as important as removing the damage. In a converted building, repairs are necessary to damp-proof, weather, insulate and ventilate it. All of which should prevent fungal attack in the future if done properly. You might consider your restoration work to be the primary measure when treating fungal outbreaks. The secondary measure would be a physical treatment of all remaining timbers and walls within the affected zone. But any treatment of retained elements can only follow the removal of the affected ones, and in the case of dry rot removal this means burning the material away from the building.

Specialist companies that are members of the British Wood Preserving and Damp-proofing Association work to a code of practice for these remedial treatments, and they should be able to survey and diagnose, as well as treat.

Renovating suspended timber ground floors

You might feel happier removing a timber ground floor entirely and replacing it with a concrete one, but this is hardly ever necessary. If damage has occurred it is usually because of the lack of ventilation beneath the floor or dampness at the walls. Once the floorboards are lifted, a true inspection can be made of their condition. You should be looking for the following:

◆ any wet or dry rot, darkening or whitening of the timbers
◆ smell
◆ whether the joists are sitting above a damp-proof course at the wall bearings
◆ whether the joists have been damaged by excessive drilling and notching, or partition walls built off them are causing deflection

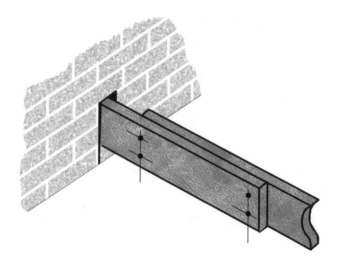

◄ A splice repair to a joist.

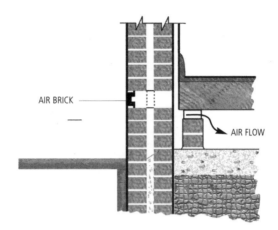

AIR BRICK

AIR FLOW

▶ Good cross-ventilation beneath timber floors is essential to avoid decay.

◆ whether you can feel the movement of air beneath the boards – good ventilation can be felt as well as seen
◆ whether the voids been filled with dirt, ash and waste over the years and are in need of clearing out

Even assuming all is OK, before you replace the boards the floor will need to be insulated between the joists. The old floorboards may be solid, but they will have gaps and knot holes here and there, making them draughty and a source of heat loss. It depends on your choice of insulation material as to how you install it since they all need supporting in some way. Glass-wool and mineral-wool quilts can be set into chicken-wire trays draped and pinned between the joists to the depth of the insulation, but rigid foam

ALUMINIUM FOIL LAMINATION SHEET   PHENOLIC FOAM INSULATION BOARD

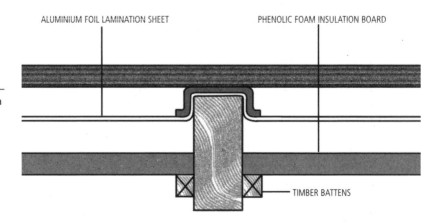

▶ Cross-section through floor showing insulation and draught-sealing.

TIMBER BATTENS

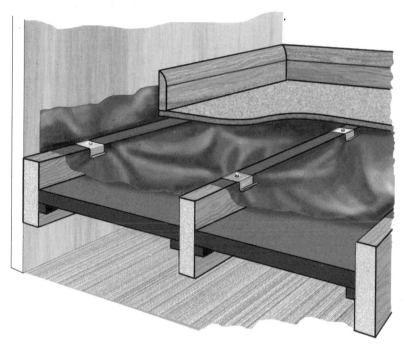

◀ An insulated
timber ground
floor.

boards cannot simply be wedged in; they need to be supported on
battens, nailed to the side of the joists. Both of these materials can
be thought of as rodent food or nesting material, and mice are
likely to have access to these voids whether you like it or not. I
would use an aluminium multi-laminate insulation as a top-up
and support sheet. It can be dressed over the top of the joists and
pinned in place. Although the insulation quality of these products
is variable and insufficient alone, they will dramatically improve
the resistance to heat loss by forming a draught- and vapour-
resistant layer beneath the thicker insulation. Most are now sold
as supplementary products.

CHAPTER 2

With planning permission granted, it is time to look at the legalities and technicalities of home dividing. Whether it be the straightforward conversion of a garage to an annexe or the complex compartmentation of a Victorian mews into apartments, regulations abound. Exactly which ones are applicable will vary from project to project, but some will have a more profound influence than others and are well worth viewing in advance.

Building Regulations

In dividing homes, and indeed in most aspects of working on buildings and their services, you are required to comply with the requirements of the Building Regulations. These regulations impose health and safety, energy efficiency and accessibility requirements on to the built environment. Providing you meet these minimum standards in the design and construction of your proposal, you will receive Building Regulation approval.

Full plans approval

Building Regulation approval has to be applied for, but it is a significantly different process to that of planning. The Building Control service is available from your local council or from an Approved Inspector – a private company licensed by the government to act as a Building Control body – so you have a choice in which to use.

The control service has two elements to it: a plans check and inspections on site. With full plans approval, you can expect them to write to you setting out a list of defects or amendments that need to be made to the plans before approval is given. Alternatively, they may simply make these points the subject of a conditional approval. Either way, these should be resolved and included in the contract before work starts so that you avoid problems on site later. In submitting a full plans application, you will have the benefit of working from plans and a specification that you know comply with the standards. The Building Regulations become more and more complex with each passing year; if you follow the specification, you can avoid problems and even abortive work. But you do have a choice, as you are eligible to submit a Building Notice instead of full plans. In Scotland, the notice of approval is known as a Building Warrant.

Building Notice

The Building Notice is simply a statement form that says that you will be complying with the Building Regulations in executing the work, and gives the building control authority two days' notice of

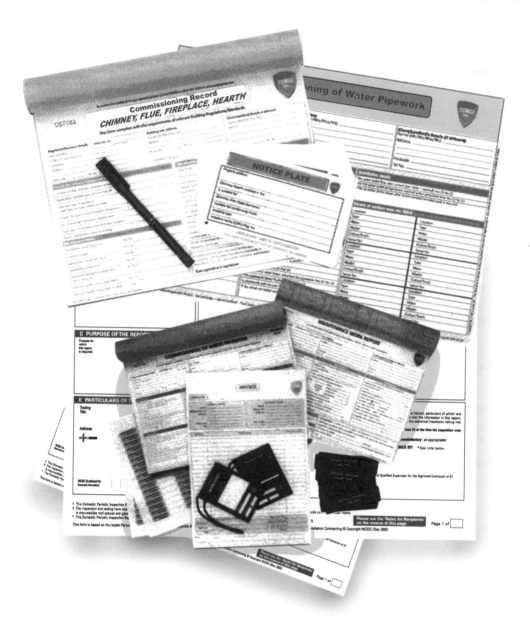

your intention to start the work. The authority will inspect the work at various stages on your notification and advise you of any contraventions as they occur. The Building Notice relies solely on the inspection service to establish whether the work complies, and hence you will have little idea of what will be needed and how much it will cost beforehand.

Apart from the form (and fee), you will need to submit a block plan with the drainage proposals indicated and the siting of the building on the plot. The notice procedure is not available in Scotland.

▲ An essential part of home dividing is acquiring all the relevant approvals and certificates at every stage.

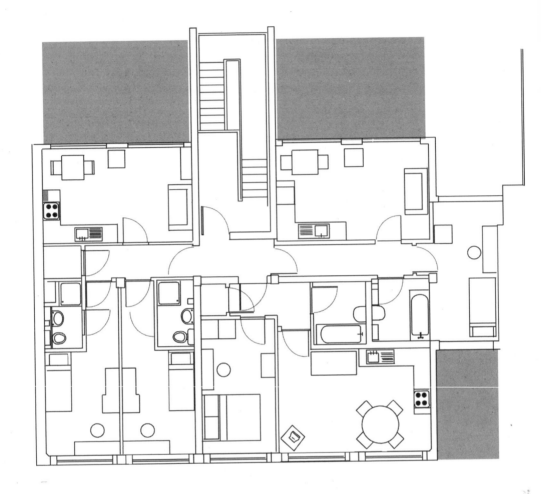

▲ Typical
two-door
arrangement
with apartment
entrances from
a communal
staircase and an
internal lobby
to each
apartment.

A big element of risk goes hand in hand with adopting the Building Notice method. Without the benefit of approved plans to work to, you have no assurance that your scheme will comply with current regulations. Your building-control surveyor may know you have contravened a requirement only once you have done so, and it could prove costly to rectify.

Advice on Building Regulations

If you need any advice on particular requirements of the Building Regulations, the building control section of your local authority will be only too pleased to help. In England and Wales, the requirements are contained in a series of 'Approved Documents' lettered A to P (parts B and L are in multiple parts) and issued by the department of Communities and Local Government (CLG) as guides to compliance. Each one deals with separate issues. For example, Part A relates to structure, while Part B is in two volumes and covers fire spread (Volume 1 (dwellings) applies to annexes and Volume 2 (non-dwellings) covers flats and maisonettes). Part C covers resistance to weather and ground moisture. Although Part L comes in four parts, only one (L1B) applies to work on existing dwellings. These are the guides for energy conservation, and they are hefty.

The Approved Documents can be purchased from the HMSO or any good bookshop, and are available as free downloads from the CLG website (www.communities.gov.uk). They are also usually found in the reference section of public libraries.

Competent persons and self-certification

The government's competent-person scheme has been established for a few years now and grows continually. It allows certain trades with qualified and competent individuals to become registered and able to self-certify their own work. If work covered by such trades was all that you were having done, you could save yourself the expense of a Building Regulations application by using a tradesperson registered in this fashion. As dividing homes amounts to a change of use or building work, however, a formal application to a Building Control body for approval under the building regulations will always be needed. Even so, for added assurance, you would be well advised to seek out people registered under the competent-person scheme for at least some of the work, even when you are going through the Building Regulations application process. This applies in particular to electricians, as well as gas, oil and solid-fuel appliance installers who are registered. There are a number of companies (and organisations) that have schemes for their members to join which mean competent-person status for the individual. Corporate membership is not possible – this is on an individual basis only. Remember, though, that there is nothing to be gained from using registered window installers, as this particular scheme is corporately managed for administrative convenience and offers no assurance of quality.

Site inspections

As your building work proceeds, the building-control surveyor must inspect it at various stages. Notice has to be given to the surveyor and the work at these stages left exposed for inspection before it is covered up and the work continued. The surveyor is usually able to avoid causing delays if he or she is given enough lead time for booking in the inspection.

The stages for notification usually include:

1.	commencement	2 days' notice
2.	foundation excavation	1 day's notice
3.	foundation concrete	1 day's notice
4.	oversite preparation	1 day's notice
5.	DPC (damp proof course)	1 day's notice
6.	drains before covering	1 day's notice
7.	drains testing	1 day's notice
8.	occupation	1 day's notice
9.	completion	2 days' notice

Some authorities may require additional inspection notices, such as exposure of existing foundations, so check with them before starting. Commencing and completing notices should be in writing, and most authorities provide cards that can be used for this purpose. E-mail or fax are excellent ways of giving notice as they endorse the request with the time and date it is transmitted. Some authorities may operate a telephoned notice system. If you do not receive an inspection within the time limit, it is extremely unwise to carry on without first contacting the building-control office to check why a surveyor has not come out, and giving them an eleventh-hour opportunity to do so. Trying to rush ahead may only mean having to expose work that has been covered up when it is inspected further down the track.

Building-control officers do not supervise the work on your behalf. They carry out spot checks to ensure that the minimum standards of the Building Regulations have been met in the interests of health, safety and energy efficiency. If you are in any doubt as to the quality of your builder's workmanship, you should appoint your own surveyor to oversee the project. A private surveyor can ensure quality control of the work, authorising stage payments as the job proceeds.

Certificates

Once the work is finished, a completion certificate should be sought from your building-control office. This is a valuable piece of paper that is required before you occupy, sell, let or remortgage the property. It is a statement that the newly divided home complies with the Building Regulations. Until this point, you may have only a plans approval notice stating that your plans comply. On completion, you will have to submit a sheath of paperwork to your building-control office for examination. This takes the form of certificates, which may include Electrical Part P, emergency lighting, fire-alarm system, gas safety, SAP (energy rating) and sound-testing certification. The building-control office then issues the completion certificate in return.

Your SAP rating does not ordinarily need to reach a certain level, but it must be produced and displayed for potential owners and tenants to see. As a mark of energy efficiency, it will translate into a measure of how much it will cost them to heat the new home and provide hot water. A 'carbon-index' figure is given with it on a scale of 0 to 10; the lower that figure, the better.

SAP calculations can also be used as a design tool for overcoming problems. Perhaps the walls cannot be upgraded to the required level or the windows are too large in comparison to the floor area. In these situations, the excessive heat loss through one element can be 'traded off' through a more than necessary upgrade in another. The way to illustrate that your proposal works is by using SAP calculations that look at each divided home and its carbon emissions as a whole, then comparing them with a notional home based on the actual minimum requirements. If your proposal has the same or less carbon released over a year, it will comply.

Sound tests on the separating floors and walls between homes (not annexes) are required to reach a certain level unless the building is registered as a listed building, in which case the reduced standard achieved should be displayed for potential owners and tenants.

If you are planning to let or lease your divided home, there are other regulatory matters to consider on top of the Building Regulations.

Landlords and tenants

The reforms that have taken place in recent years have left local authorities with sweeping powers over landlords. Tenanted properties these days have to meet a much higher standard than before, which can only be a good thing. Unfortunately, the landlords who slip through the net are always the same ones – those who defy any attempt by the local authority to have improvements carried out and those who have a regular tenancy base of immigrants, people on welfare and others clinging on to whatever they can get. These tenants are always vulnerable in the private sector. Landlords always have the right to give a notice of termination to their lease and cast them out if they complain too much. Conversely, when you look at how much damage some tenants do to a property, you can understand why this power is so frequently used, but it is also abused to threaten tenants who complain of genuine health and safety infringements to the local council. Housing authorities have the power to enforce improvements they see necessary in health and safety terms – adequate ventilation, fire safety, weather tightness and insulation, for example. If landlords fail to carry out upgrading works within a certain time span after being served with an improvement order, they could see the property being improved by council-appointed builders and the costs passed on to them. Failure to pay could mean the debt is transferred to the land registry as a charge on the sale of it at any time in the future.

From the landlord's point of view, getting rid of unruly tenants or those that fail to pay the rent is not that easy. In some cases, those who have failed to leave after due notice have had to be evicted by other methods. I mention all this because the business of being a landlord is not always plain sailing. Finding perfect tenants that respect the property, look after it and pay the rent on time is the ambition for all landlords. You cannot categorise the type of tenant that will respect your property and the type that will destroy it. There are no stereotypes. I recently visited a Victorian property divided into four flats which was under refurbishment where some of the period features in the common hallway had been vandalised by a wayward tenant. Why anyone would attack plaster cornicing, staircase balustrading and an antique mirror was beyond understanding, but the sad fact of it is – some people do.

Renting out

When you consider renting out accommodation, you need to know your market. That is to say, you need to know the market that exists in your location; not the one you would like to exist. The television shows that follow people through their first steps of property development have them all marketing to 'young professionals'. The idea of young people out all day at work earning shedloads of money to pay their rent and keeping the place immaculately clean while barely living in it is an attractive one to any would-be landlord. I do not know how many 'young professionals' there are roaming the streets for rented accommodation these days, but there is no point in creating a lavishly designed apartment for them if they do not exist in your area. It may be that there are more students, nurses, people on low incomes or benefits in your town than advertising executives who cannot or prefer not to invest in their own property. Local estate agents and management agencies will tell you where the demand is, whether it be for studio bed-sits or three-bedroom mews apartments.

Students in term-time accommodation are protected as tenants in HMOs (see below) in the same way as anybody would be in full-time residence. Indeed, many universities take an active role in ensuring that their students are housed in suitable licensed property and will carry out checks. The on-campus accommodation that universities themselves provide is usually restricted to first-year students; after that they prefer them to seek accommodation off-campus and will be keen to know of suitable places in the locality.

HMOs and the property licence system

A new system for controlling HMOs (homes in multiple occupation) has been introduced and it is the property licence system. The old system had been in place for a long time and was out of date decades ago. The system replacing it is an attempt to raise the standards in the private rental sector by shaking off some of the dodgy landlords and fixing a decent minimum standard. Badly managed HMOs have been responsible for reduced property values in some areas, with neglected, unmaintained buildings lining some streets and generally creating a down-at-heel feel to the place. Creating HMOs to a good standard and keeping them there costs money, and many landlords were looking to maximise their profit even at the expense of their tenant's health and safety.

In 2006, the government changed the system for controlling landlords and HMOs. I have always found the legislation surrounding HMOs to be out of date, confusing and nonsensical. It has been improved with the Housing Act 1984, as this act refers to the Building Regulations for some illustration of compliance. Previously, the enforcing officers (usually environmental-health officers) were at sea when it came to guidance and had to resort to Home Office guides, advice from fire-safety officers and scratching their heads. Fire-safety officers stopped helping them out some years ago when they were told that they should not be doing design work (at least not free of charge), and the Home Office guides have become seriously out of date and out of tune with other, more contemporary guides.

The first puzzle to solve is what constitutes an HMO. Think bed-sits and communal sharing of facilities – kitchen-down-the-hall-type student accommodation, and not self-contained apartments with their own kitchens and bathrooms. If you are about to divide up a building into self-contained apartments as individual households that comply with the Building Regulations of today (as indeed you must), then it is not going to be an HMO.

A self-contained apartment by definition is one that has a kitchen (cooking area), bathroom and toilet for the exclusive use of the people residing there. Those people must fall into the definition of a 'household', which I will explain a bit later, but essentially that cannot be a large number of friends sharing together. That would be an HMO, which is why the subletting of apartments by tenants to other people, friends or not, is such a problem. It redefines the laws surrounding the property. You could, however, include a nanny or an au pair into a household as 'staff'. Family members can be deemed to include stepchildren, adopted children, grandchildren, grandparents and civil partners, as well as brothers, sisters, uncles, aunts, nephews and nieces. When you begin to include the 'cousins' branch of the family tree, you have fallen outside the definition. It still leaves plenty of scope for extended family living outside of the property licence regulations.

Ordinarily, dividing your home up for members of the same family will not make it an HMO, and consequently much of the content of this book is outside of the property-licence scenario. You may also create accommodation for up to two unrelated lodgers without your home becoming an HMO. Three or more and it will be.

Do you need a property licence?
At the heart of this new legislation is the 'property licence'. Although an HMO is defined by the number of households (and just two single people living separately in a building equates to two households), not all HMOs need a property licence. There has to be a certain scale to the building and its occupation to qualify. The criteria for those that do are:

◆ three or more storeys
◆ five or more tenants
◆ in two or more households

All three of those criteria need to be met; not just one or two of them. Governments are prone to changing their minds and their rules, however, and therefore it is essential that you check with your local authority regarding your division project to see whether a licence is required. Also, each local authority can run its own licensing scheme, in addition to and outside of the mandatory one, and you may be obliged to consider that too.

The standard for achieving a licence

A minimum standard must be met for a licence to be granted. In
the past this was known as the Fitness for Human Habitation
Standard. As you may have gathered from the title, it was a basic
check to ensure such things as water supply, sanitary facilities,
daylight and air were available to the tenants. The new test is very
different and carried out on a rating basis of health and safety
known, equally as literally, as the Housing Health and Safety
Rating System (HHSRS).

Instead of setting out minimum standards of health and safety,
the test identifies hazards and categorises them. The very worst
hazards (category 1) have to be absent to obtain a licence. If any
are present, the licence will not be issued.

Irrespective of the property condition, the landlord has to meet
a test as well. To be eligible for a licence, a landlord has to be 'a
fit and proper person'. The definition of what constitutes a fit and
proper person as far as the Housing Act is concerned relates to
matters such as any criminal offences that lie as unspent
convictions, demonstrated racism or contraventions to housing,
tenant or landlord law. These things will be looked into and
judgements made as to whether they will affect your application.

How to obtain a property licence

Local authorities are able to set their own fees to fund the scheme
for applications, and consequently the cost from one area to
another can differ greatly. The licence applies to a property, rather
than a landlord; if you have several HMOs under your belt, each
property will require a separate licence. Having said that, you
cannot pass the licence on with the property should you choose to
sell it. The new owner will need to apply for his or her own licence.

As the person who receives the rent, you are the licence holder,
and to obtain a licence you must make an application to the local
authority. As with planning and Building Regulation applications,
you can apply through an agent (perhaps a letting agent) who
may hold the property on your behalf. The environmental health
section (which has traditionally dealt with HMOs) of your local
authority usually deals with property licences.

Licences will usually last for five years (three years in Scotland),
after which you will need to reapply. When you do, a notice will
be displayed outside of the premises similar to those you see when
planning applications have been submitted, and local residents
will be able to object. As with planning applications, objections
from neighbours are taken into account, but do not necessarily
have a bearing on the decision.

The local authority and the local fire safety officer may inspect the premises when applications are received to check on the building's condition. They can also impose occupancy limits on your licence to reduce the number of people living in the property. They could also impose conditions requiring you to upgrade the amenities or facilities within a set time frame. Where they consider that nothing can be done to bring the building up to scratch within a reasonable time, they may simply refuse your licence. Having your licence suspended or revoked means that you will not be able to continue using the building as an HMO and your tenants may have to move out. The local authority will be responsible for finding them alternative accommodation.

Running an HMO without a property licence is a criminal offence that carries a hefty fine.

Gas Safety Regulations

In providing gas appliances to the new home, you are responsible for maintaining those appliances under the Gas Safety Regulations, which apply not only to installing gas appliances, but also to maintaining them fit for use. Annual checks and servicing by a CORGI-registered installer on each appliance and flue are duties placed on landlords by this legislation. It applies to any home held under licence, tenancy agreement or short-term lease. As landlord, you should keep a record of each safety check for at least two years and issue a copy of each to the tenant within 28 days of the check being completed. Appliances that are owned by the tenant are not the landlord's responsibility.

The Crown Court imposes hefty fines on landlords who do not maintain appliances – quite rightly so given the risk to life that faulty appliances bring.

Electrical safety and periodic inspections

In addition to gas safety inspections, electrical safety inspections must be done periodically by a qualified and registered electrician who is able to issue a Periodic Inspection Report with reference to BS: 7671 (IEE Wiring Regulations). It has been specifically designed for checking existing installations only and not for carrying out new work. The purpose of the report should be stated on it, which could be to ascertain compliance with the current wiring regulations or perhaps simply to report on the safety condition of the cabling and equipment.

Make sure that you and your electrician agree what the purpose is and check that it is stated on the forms. The extent and any limitations of the report should also be clearly stated, although these should not appear in the form of a surprise – your contractor should have made you aware beforehand. Reports are usually formed in sections and include the test results on the circuits, earthing arrangements and circuit breakers. Observations and recommendations are detailed and awarded ratings of priority for action.

FOUR RATINGS FOR PRIORITISING ACTION
1. Requires urgent attention
2. Requires improvement
3. Requires further investigation
4. Does not comply with IEE Wiring Regulations (current edition), but this does not mean the installation is unsafe for use

Your tenants and their rights

If your tenants are paying you rent (either directly or through a letting agency) and they share the HMO with other tenants, then they are classed as either an 'assured tenant' or a 'short assured tenant'. As with all tenants (not just those in HMOs), you have to ensure their legal rights as such, and indeed the local authority has to check that you respect their legal rights. Part of that means providing any tenants with a written tenancy agreement that sets out clearly who is responsible for what.

As a landlord you are required to:

◆ keep the property in a good state of repair (including any fittings and furniture you provide)
◆ deal fairly and lawfully with tenants over rent and payments, and that includes following set procedures if you want to increase their rent, not surcharging gas or electricity provided to tenants, not withholding their deposits unnecessarily and not evicting them illegally

There is also one other issue that frightens landlords: you are responsible for ensuring that your tenants do not annoy or upset other people living in the area through their behaviour. Before you grow too alarmed, the reality of this responsibility might not be as bad as you think. If they are making a lot of noise, for example, you can warn them not to and, if they persist, notify the environmental health's pollution control section, which will engage procedures against them. Thus you have fulfilled your obligations.

Your tenants also have responsibilities of their own. They include:

◆ notifying you of anything that needs repairing, particularly such things as the roof, boiler or the toilet, which you have statutory duties to maintain

◆ taking good care of the property and trying not to damage anything

◆ ensuring that rubbish does not pile up and is disposed of properly in provided bins

◆ allowing the landlord access for maintenance inspections (usually once very six months) after 24 hours' notice has been provided

◆ not behaving in a way likely to upset neighbours

Occupancy numbers

As the landlord, it is your responsibility to control and limit the number of people residing in your property. Tenants are allowed to have short-term non-paying guests, but are not allowed to have long-term occupants move in. This is often the case with young people, who may have girlfriends or boyfriends move in during the tenancy.

Information to occupiers

Tenants and home buyers alike have something in common: they move into their new home knowing nothing about it. Most have had a brief guided tour and some are given an information card, but generally it is all a bit poor. Moves are afoot to introduce a home buyers pack that gives all the information needed, but of course people generally prefer to be shown rather than given a ton of technical reading material to wade through. I would recommend you provide a home info pack outlining the basics, but take the time to show people around and explain things. Important information that should be included in both is:

◆ where the stopcock is for turning off the water

◆ how to operate and programme the central heating and hot-water controls

◆ where the meters are (gas, electricity and water)

◆ how to operate fire egress, child-safety and easy-clean window hinges and trickle vents

◆ how to operate door locks

◆ how to operate the shower

◆ appliance manuals

◆ how to operate any white goods provided

◆ the home's energy (SAP) rating

◆ tenants' information on responsibilities for maintenance
◆ tenants' contact details for reporting problems
◆ how to change circuit breakers and reset RCDs on the electrical circuit
◆ how to check the smoke alarms
◆ how often the boiler/central heating should be serviced
◆ when and to what extent tenants can install their own fixtures and fittings
◆ what, if any, decorating tenants can do within the property

Although freehold is the most common form of tenure in the United Kingdom, leasehold is not unusual when it comes to smaller homes such as apartments. When buildings are divided up into smaller dwellings, the building as a whole and the land it sits on can lose some of its identity. To secure its future, it is usually retained as the freehold tenure of the owner. The owner may be known as the freeholder or the lessor, but more commonly as the landlord. The apartments or maisonettes may then be individually leased to others. A lease is a right to use the building or part of it for a period of time, and the person it is granted to is known as the lessee or more commonly as the tenant.

It is possible to sell an apartment on a freehold basis under a new tenure known as a 'commonhold'. Introduced in 1994, the commonhold principle is entirely different from leasehold and quite unusual. It was introduced to provide an alternative method of ownership and management in blocks of flats, and it is controlled by Her Majesty's Court Service (contact details are provided on page 254).

The principal acts of parliament you should be aware of are:

◆ Landlord and Tenant Act 1985
◆ Landlord and Tenant Act 1987
◆ Leasehold Reform, Housing and Urban Development Act 1993
◆ Housing Act 1996
◆ Commonhold and Leasehold Reform Act 2002
◆ Building Act 1984

CHAPTER 3

DIVIDING HOMES

Some technical issues are at the fore when a building is physically divided up into homes, and this applies to two areas in particular: sound insulation and fire resistance. Both play a role right from the initial stages of design because they have a strong bearing on how you plan and divide up the property. Consequently, the lines of division need to be drawn first, and there is much to consider.

Dividing lines

When it comes to annexes, it really does not matter how you or where you separate the home, as space can be burrowed from anywhere it exists to achieve the accommodation you need. This is not so in the case of apartments and maisonettes. When homes are being divided into separate self-contained dwellings, it is important to separate them cleanly with straight lines of either vertical separation (walls) or horizontal separation (floors). Mixing the two in the same building is not helpful.

Imagine that you create a ground-floor apartment with a smaller apartment in the basement below it. The basement apartment only sits below part of the ground-floor home above, not all of it. A section of the floor, perhaps in one room of the ground-floor apartment, extends to 'over sail' part of the basement. As a result that bit of the ground-floor apartment acquires a separating floor requiring both fire and sound resistance, which technically the rest of the floor does not. The arrangement could also create a 'flying tenancy' or, worse still, a flying freehold, and neither is a desirable asset. Every once in a while, I meet somebody whose home has a lump in the party wall or a bulkhead in the ceiling where a bit of next door's kitchen comes through. Or perhaps the upper floor is bigger than the floor below because it sits over the neighbour's lounge instead of theirs. Such things were irreversibly created in history when bits of buildings were sold off to neighbours, but you do not create them today if you can avoid it.

Anomalies such as this are to be avoided at all costs. When you are creating apartments or maisonettes as self-contained dwellings, it is a case of having to think in boxes because straight lines in dividing homes are so much better.

Dividing against noise

Sound, like light, travels in waves. It may consist only of tiny fluctuations in the atmospheric pressure surrounding us, but these small pressure variations are recognised by our ears and converted into the sensation we call hearing. This phenomenon is unique in the way it is measured and indeed received by us, on a logarithmic

scale. We use decibels as the unit for measuring sound. The higher
the number of decibels, the louder the sound is, starting from 0
decibels at the threshold of hearing and ending at 120 decibels at
the threshold of pain. From about 60 decibels upwards, noise can
cause stress, sleep loss and psychological disorders. There have
even been studies that conclude that people who are exposed to
65 decibels and more every day will have a 20 per cent higher risk
of suffering a heart attack from the increased stress noise has
placed on them. When we are subjected to continuous noise, our
bodies may produce a stream of adrenaline leading to
hypertension and stress-related problems. To put it simply, noise is
not good for us, and yet it has been calculated that almost two-
thirds of the population of Europe is regularly exposed to noise
over 55 decibels, and 16 per cent of people are often subjected to
noise over the critical 65-decibel limit. The reason for sound
insulation in our homes becomes clear now: our home is our
sanctuary and the one place where we hope to escape the stresses
of modern life. Having some peace and quiet is a big part of
achieving that. Indeed, some surveys have also confirmed that,
after fire protection, sound insulation is an area where new home
owners are unwilling to compromise.

Sound insulation

One of the most onerous requirements of your project will come
from achieving the sound insulation that must exist between
homes today. Homes that are situated on top of each other have
to rely on the floor construction to meet these standards, and that
is where much of the budget goes. There are four elements to
achieving good sound insulation: mass, resilience, isolation and air
space. If you pay attention to all four (and not simply one or
two), you should be successful. Adding weight to the construction
increases the mass, making it soft increases the resilience, isolating
it reduces the width of the path that sound can travel along and
including an air space puts an end to that path.

Horizontal separation – dividing floors

When it comes to achieving sound insulation, floors can perform
badly. They always need work if they are to make the grade.
Traditional floors in our homes are constructed hollow, with
timber joists covered by boarding and a thin layer of plasterboard
or plaster lathe beneath for the ceiling. This is a construction that
offers hardly any resistance to noise. Upgrading floors to the
acceptable standard is possible, but not without expense and a
good deal of effort. But not only do you have to do it to comply

with the Building Regulations, when you separate dwellings in this way, you have to have the work tested when it is finished to prove that it is working as it should do and both the design and workmanship adopted have been successful. Sound testing of floors falls into two parts; airborne sound test and impact sound test. This can be expensive because it requires a registered consultant (with specialist equipment) and the ability to self-certify the results.

Airborne sound might be voices, music or televisions playing loudly next door. These days, entertainment systems come equipped with deep thumping bass tones (and the test has to simulate those low frequencies, too). In order to create those bass tones, multifaceted speakers blast out pink noise at ear-piercing volume. Unlike walls, floors are able to transmit more than one type of noise; as well as airborne sound, impact sound can also pass through them. Impact sound is the sound of footfalls or the moving of furniture, for example. It is, in fact, simulated during the sound test by a machine with mechanical dancing feet that frantically pummel the floor. Like the airborne sound test, it is

▸ Over-floor sound matting used in conjunction with insulation between joists and resilient bars to ceiling.

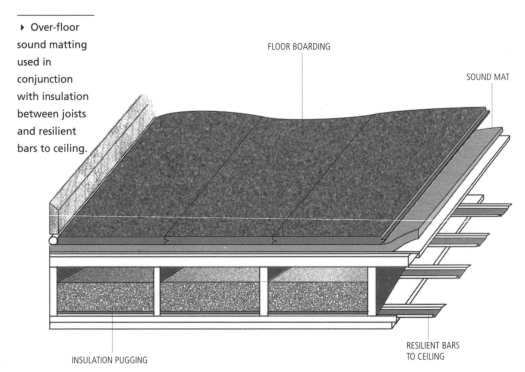

FLOOR BOARDING

SOUND MAT

RESILIENT BARS TO CEILING

INSULATION PUGGING

unrealistically loud, but the point of these tests is not to see what can be eliminated, but how much sound is being cut out. The Building Regulations require sound reduction of a certain amount, not sound elimination.

Before the Building Regulations began to address the issue of sound insulation, you would have struggled to find sound-deadening products on the market. The most common method of insulating a floor historically was with sand, poured between the joists. This was known as 'pugging' and was not ineffective, but obviously given the weight of sand you could use only about 50 mm (2 in) of it. Now the market is awash with hi-tech products, and nobody has to install a beach in their ceiling any more.

Choosing your approach

With so many sound-improving materials and systems available, your first decision has to be whether to work from above or below. Some products are designed to sit on top of the floor and others below the ceiling. For those on top, you have to consider what the implications will be of raising the floor finish. Doors

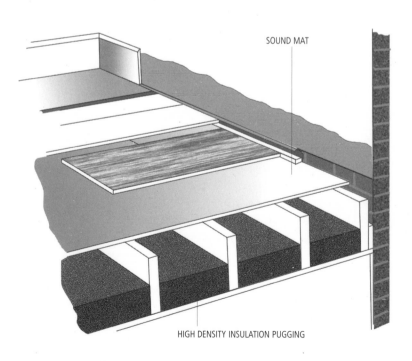

SOUND MAT

HIGH DENSITY INSULATION PUGGING

◀ Over-floor systems for sound insulation often need additional insulation between the joists.

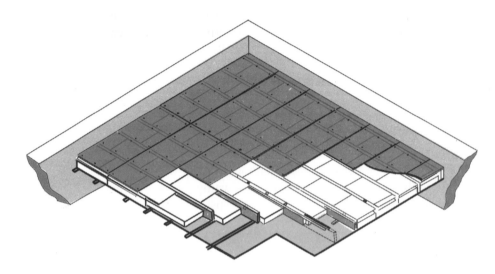

▲ Exploded
view of a
sound-
improvement
system to a
floor.

may have to be removed and trimmed down, and door frames
and skirting boards removed and refixed. Working from above
can even affect the stairs, increasing the top step to an
unacceptable degree.

Working beneath the floor by replacing the ceilings is more
common, but it is not without problems. The ceiling is inevitably
lowered, and cornicings or covings may be lost. Cables for light
fittings may have to be extended or relocated, and in general
ceiling work is messy and disruptive. It also depends on having
high-enough ceilings to begin with. The distance between the top
of your window openings and the existing ceiling needs to be at
least 100 mm, so that it does not look odd when it is lowered.
Installing new ceilings or at least finishing them with plaster is
skilled work, whereas working above can be easy DIY work, and
hence you have to appraise both the material cost and the labour
before deciding which route to follow. Once you have made that
decision, you can start to look for a system that works.

Working from above

If you have a fairly level floor to work with, probably the easiest
treatment is to overlay it with one of the heavy resilient layer
materials. Some are attached to boarding; others come on a roll
and are covered with a new floor of tongue-and-groove flooring-
grade chipboard. In all cases they simply 'float' on top; although

as the tongues are glued into the grooves of each board, no other fixing is required. In fact, fixing down the layer is going to create a sound path and defeat the object of the treatment. The resilient roll-out layers vary in thickness, but typically anything between 6 mm and 12 mm is common, depending on the material (which is likely to be foam plastic or rubber-based). The skirting boards will pin the finished floor down via an acoustic flanking strip, avoiding direct contact between the skirting boards and the floorboarding.

Take some time to look into any product you see because they vary hugely in expected performance. You could use the foam kind of underlay employed under laminate floors and undoubtedly this will have some acoustic value, but it will not be nearly enough by itself. Most, if not all, topside floor methods require more work to be done between the floor joists, as well as on top of them. Typically 100 mm or more of dense mineral insulation pugging is used, and this is much denser than the thermal insulation quilt you may be used to seeing in lofts. Pugging is required to tackle airborne sound and to reduce its transmission through the floor void. It can be supported on sound-quality plasterboard planks that are themselves laid as shelves on battens fixed to the side of joists or on resilient metal bars that straddle them. Like sand, these materials work by mass; the greater the density of both plasterboard and insulation, the greater the sound reduction and resistance to airborne sound. What really helps, though, is making sure that they fit snugly in places and that there are no gaps between them and the sides of the joists. Acoustic mastic can be used to seal around the edges of the plasterboard.

Plasterboard that is heavier than normal has been made for use in dividing homes by the principal manufacturers. When you have lifted a few sheets of it, you will appreciate the difference between it and ordinary plasterboard. Often it is slightly thicker as well. As I mentioned earlier, you can isolate it from the joists themselves and reduce the transmittance through the support by using resilient metal bars.

The plank boards can be laid onto metal shelves that are fixed to the joists. This isolation of the plank (pugging) board from the joists helps again to improve the sound insulation. The resilient shelves themselves are made from thin galvanised metal, perhaps only a millimetre or so thick. Although they sit over the joists, the boards can be re-nailed over them without raising the floor. As you can see in the illustration (page 68), the metal shelves are shaped like a top hat to allow the plasterboard planks to sit below the floorboard. In building construction terms, this is fragile work. Although the floor level is restored to the top of the joists before the floorboarding is laid, there is little strength in the deck and you do need to work off a catwalk. Scaffold boards or floor sheets that can be moved about are essential – tiptoeing on the joist tops never works for me.

Working from below

Under-drawn ceilings

Much of what needs to be done depends on what exists at present. Ceilings that are in good condition need not be torn down. Indeed, lathe and plaster ceilings are very helpful to sound resistance. Leaving them in situ where they can contribute to sound- and fire-proofing makes perfect sense as long as they are finished to a reasonable level. Just as there are resilient caps that you can fit to the tops of joists, there are resilient bars that you fit

▸ Over-joist clips used to add plasterboard beneath the floor boarding.

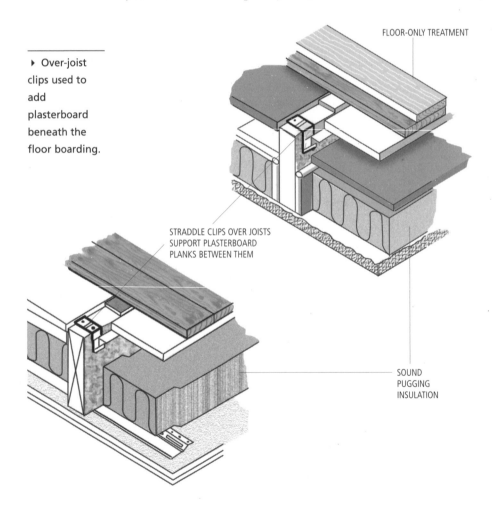

FLOOR-ONLY TREATMENT

STRADDLE CLIPS OVER JOISTS
SUPPORT PLASTERBOARD
PLANKS BETWEEN THEM

SOUND
PUGGING
INSULATION

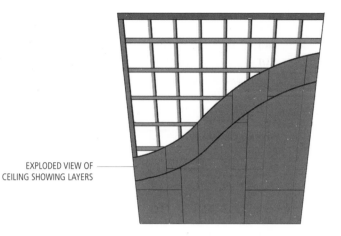

EXPLODED VIEW OF
CEILING SHOWING LAYERS

◄ Double layer
plasterboard
ceiling on
resilient bars
screwed to
joists.

to ceilings to isolate the new layers. These are thin metal strips with rubber seating to cushion the fixing between the materials. These strips of metal will take a self-tapping screw, anchoring the plasterboard in place, but they themselves need to be well fixed to the timber joists. Adequately spaced across the joists (not along them), they will be available at board joints for fixing both sheets of new plasterboard. That may be two layers of sound-reducing board or one of sound- and one of fire-rated board to finish. In the case of home division projects, working in existing buildings means that usually you can use materials with only 30 minutes of fire-resistance to protect the floor, rather than the 60 minutes required in new-build construction. As it happens, you will probably achieve the one hour rating by accident, simply because of the sound deadening. Although these two layers will help, they may not be enough without adding some sound pugging insulation in-between the joists, and that, of course, will mean taking up the floorboards.

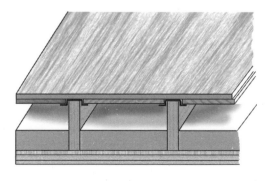

◄ Combined
floor and
ceiling
treatment.

Independent ceilings

If lifting the floorboarding was not planned and seems like too much trouble, leaving the floor above untouched is possible in some cases. Where existing ceilings are higher than normal (normal is about 2.3 m) and you can afford the headroom, an independent suspended ceiling can be formed beneath the original one. This new ceiling would be supported by its own structure of new timber joists that span from wall to wall and are not in contact with the existing joists or ceiling above. A minimum gap between the two of 25 mm is advisable.

The joists themselves are likely to be smaller than the floor joists because they will be supporting only a fraction of the weight – about a quarter of the load on a domestic floor. The weight of sound-reducing materials, however, is not inconsiderable. The plasterboard and insulation plus the weight of the joists themselves is the total load they will have to support, and the framework will be done on a room by room basis with the joists spanning in the shortest direction to keep the depth down. Frequently, 50 x 100 mm joists are sufficient, but it is important to assess the load and have them checked for adequacy. Using C24 grade timbers will also help, as this has a higher stress grading than C16 and will allow longer spans. Two layers of 15-mm sound-quality plasterboard can amount to 26 kg per square metre, even without the insulation pugging, so make sure that your ceiling will fit.

Being able to lower the ceiling finish by 200–300 mm makes this the most practical of options. In spite of the loss of ceiling height, a secondary suspended ceiling such as this is often a sure-fire way to pass a sound test, particularly if the existing ceiling and floor finishes are in good condition. Acoustic silicone sealant or tape can be used to seal around the perimeter edges. The

JOINT SIZES AND SPANS FOR INDEPENDENT CEILINGS	
Joist sizes at 400 mm crs	Maximum span between walls for double-layered ceiling
47 x 97 C16	3.2 m
47 x 122 C16	3.9 m
47 x 147 C16	4.5 m

Crs: centres or spacing

Note Double-layered ceiling finish in table consists of:

◆ 1 layer of 12-mm sound-rated plasterboard, 1 layer of fire-rated plasterboard, 100 mm insulation (10kg/m^2)

◆ No access for maintenance.

results tend to be better than with upgrading of the existing ceiling, but you do need to be aware of chimneys, soil pipes and walls that pass through both structures and transmit sound by flanking transmission.

Dividing walls

Floors are trouble in many respects when it comes to sound insulation. Walls – less so. If you have the chance or the good fortune to divide homes vertically, then grab it. Walls are much easier to soundproof than floors, and only airborne sound must be addressed – impact does not come into it.

Walls that separate one dwelling from another are known as compartment, or separating, walls.

A brick wall will have not only around four hours worth of fire resistance, but also a decent amount of sound resistance. Brick walls that are at least 215 mm thick and rendered with dense plaster can sometimes meet the Building Regulations without any further treatment, but thinner walls or those built with less dense materials (insulating blocks) are notoriously poor from a sound transmission perspective.

▾ Independent studwork wall formed inside party wall.

If you have existing masonry walls built from firm foundations, it makes sense to utilise them as dividing walls whenever you can. Alas, internal masonry walls are a luxury that is seldom seen in modern homes, where most of the internal walls are timber stud partitions.

Upgrading brick walls can be achieved by battening the wall out with resilient metal fixing bars, between which sound-deadening mineral fibre can be pinned in place before the plasterboard is screwed to the bars and finished. A friend of mine lined his party wall in this way to reduce the noise from 'athletic' neighbours, and it worked very well. The bars are secured at the top and bottom of the wall, then spaced at a

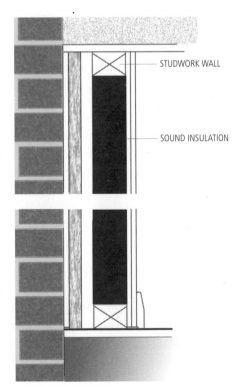

STUDWORK WALL

SOUND INSULATION

maximum of 600 mm in between. The depth of the resilient bars is important because some are so shallow that you would not get any thickness of insulation between them – at least 25 mm will be needed. If this is not possible, the wall can be battened-off first with vertical timber battens and the resilient bars secured across them. For improved sound resistance, the boarding can be upgraded from basic plasterboard to sound-insulating plasterboard to fibre-reinforced board to specialist laminated boards of greater thickness and density. It all comes down to how much sound you are trying to cut down and how much you want to pay.

In the larger Victorian home and indeed in twentieth-century houses up until the 1960s, ground- and first-floor walls were usually built from a single thickness of brick (known commonly as half-brick walls). From the 1960s onwards, the switch was made to the more economical method of building any upstairs partitions in timber studwork, clad with plasterboard. Walls may be of the same thickness, but a gentle tap will reveal whether they are hard-plastered masonry or hollow studwork.

The 1960s were not the first time we saw this kind of construction. Timber frame actually pre-dates brickwork, and was used in pre-1850 buildings. There are, however, rows of small terraced homes built in the United Kingdom by the Victorians as simple two-up/two-down cottages, split by a narrow staircase rising through the centre between the rooms. Lining the stairway on either side were thin timber stud partition walls that were clad with timber boarding, and yet the floor and indeed some of the roof was supported on these. In spite of the fact that these walls were load-bearing, they were built very cheaply and with less than the minimum materials you would need today. Often the studwork is only 50 mm (2 in) wide and the vertical match-boarding on either side is splinter-thin, but critical to stiffening the walls.

The same construction exists in the loft rooms of larger townhouses. With two or perhaps three storeys of masonry internal walls rising through the property, the uppermost floor was located within the roof space itself, lit by dormer windows. At this level it was customary to switch to building the internal walls in this way.

Oddly enough, we did go through a bit of a spell in the 1980s where we reversed this and built first-floor partitions in lightweight aerated blocks positioned upon the timber floor joists, but it was not successful for obvious reasons. Timber dries-out and when it does it shrinks, dramatically so, and the balancing masonry on it is prone to parting company with the ceilings and abutting walls.

There is one other possible wall construction that you might find in an older property – a mixture of timber studwork in-filled with bricks. This type of wall does exist, and every time I come across one I back away from it. The last one I saw rose from a basement wall at the centre of a four-storey property. This was its spinal wall and, like most spines, it supported the structure around it. The floors and walls of the storeys above, and some of the roof, were all transferred to this hybrid of timber and brick that, as you might imagine, was not tied to itself, let alone any other part of the building. The wall on each floor had a liveliness to it that you would not want in any wall, let alone a central supporting one. Quite often the nature of these structures is not apparent until the plaster is hacked-off to reveal what lies beneath, after which the wall's days are invariably numbered. Replacing it with blockwork is often the favoured solution. It means starting from the bottom and working up, perhaps from a new or underpinned foundation, but it is well worth it.

Upgrading existing partition walls to separating walls

If you have existing partition walls and need to upgrade to separating wall standards, you need to be prepared to thicken them. Taking down timber stud partitions and replacing them with masonry walls or new partitions is rarely necessary or worthwhile, but you will have to widen them with new sound improvement work.

There are different approaches to this, but perhaps the easiest is to remove the lining on one face and expose the studwork. New studs can be installed between the original ones, but set forward of them. An extension to the sole and head plates, isolated by resilient strips, will allow the new studs to create a staggered line,

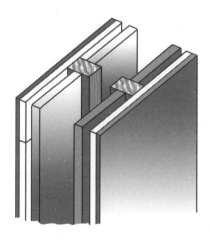

◂ Double-stud partition with boarding between and double-faced.

between which a heavy sound-deadening curtain can be interwoven. In this case, the insulation is kept thinner and heavier, and any joints are stitched together. You will be creating a staggered cavity space instead of straight one, which will buy a bit of extra space. Resilient bars are fixed and a double layer of 15-mm sound-rated plasterboard and 19-mm plank is secured to them on both sides. It will double the wall thickness, but it should be enough to resist airborne sound if it is well constructed and the insulation is correctly hung.

The chances of passing airborne tests are always reduced by existing construction; however, if specialist wall lining products are used, you can feel confident in them being successful. It pays to involve your acoustic engineer at an early stage to guide you, and likewise the manufacturers of sound insulation products, which have technical departments that are usually helpful.

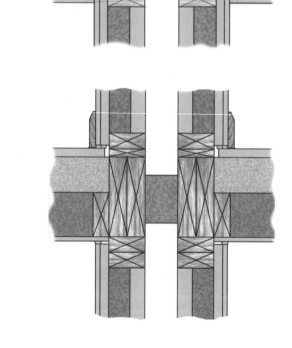

▶ Double-stud partition with insulation between and double-face plasterboarding.

▶ As above, but with an insulation stop inserted.

Timber studwork walls

If all that seems too much trouble, then taking down the partition and building a new one might be for you. Timber stud walls are the easiest of all wall constructions to build from new. They do not require foundations, are clean and fast to erect, and can be tied into the surrounding structure without damaging it. If they have a fault at all it is that people do not trust them. They seem to be the exact opposite of what we are striving to achieve: a solid and robust separation with high levels of fire and sound resistance. Actually, they are quite able to meet these standards, as long as they a built correctly and to an approved specification. Separating walls that divide dwellings such as those between apartments can be constructed in two skins of timber studwork, like a cavity wall. Once you realise that, you can see straight away how possible it is to divide homes.

The two independent stud walls are separated by a space of perhaps only 40 mm, but it is a valuable space all the same because sound will not be able to vibrate across it, as it does with solid materials. In some situations, where the ceiling height is higher than normal, it may be necessary to connect the two leaves halfway up the wall for structural reasons. It is possible to do this if a resilient brace is used that is sound isolated from the studs it connects. In normal situations, where the stud frames can be fixed independently at the peripheries, they can be kept apart entirely.

If you can obtain CLS (Canadian Lumber Standard) timber sections from your supplier, then do so. They are far better to work with than sawn wood. CLS is not only planed all round (PAR), but the corners are nicely rounded off to produce a section that is smooth and easy to handle as well. Not so long ago CLS was rare, but since 2005 it seems to have become easily obtainable and, in some cases, the standard supply, and that is a good thing indeed. Timber sections of 90 x 38 mm are adequate as long as the noggins are suitably spaced between the studs for bracing. The actual stud centres are determined by your plasterboard size, both in thickness and width of board. For 12.5-mm and 15-mm thick boards, 600-mm spacing for the studs is needed. For 9.5-mm thick boards and for any sheets that are 900 mm wide (these are the smaller plank sheets that are more manageable), you will need to bring those studs together at 450-mm centres.

Setting up the framing to suit your plasterboard is half the battle, and it pays to think it through properly before you start hammering it together. If you are uncertain, screw the studs into the sole plate at the bottom and the head plate at the top. You can then unscrew and relocate them if they are in the wrong place without damage. Armed with tape measure and pencil, marking out the sole plate with stud positions should be enough to avoid most errors. Remember that a 300-mm board width is the minimum, so do not create a situation where you end up with a thinner strip of boarding at one end if you can help it. The noggins are there to support any edges of plasterboard that you might have as well as bracing up the wall, so, if you have more than one board in height, remember to add two 38-mm wide noggins to allow both of the board ends to be fixed. It never ceases to amaze me just how much wood you need to build a stud wall, but once it is all up the plasterboard can be fixed to one side. A double layer will be essential, but before you fix it up a bead of acoustic sealant should be run around the edges of the frame to seal any gaps between the existing structure and the new wall. Boards are fixed via a resilient bar to the studs to help isolate them, and the first and last of these horizontal bars should be 50 mm from the ceiling and the floor, respectively. Drywall thread screws are needed (not plasterboard nails); these are typically 32 mm long, but this is dependent on the thickness of the board they have to penetrate.

With one side of the wall clad, you can turn your attention to the next-door face, and this will require something extra – insulation. Before plasterboarding, both stud partitions can be lagged with a semi-rigid sound insulation quilt. Some care over choosing this material must be exercised. Avoid the ones that offer thermal and sound insulation in one because they are not the same thing and therefore do not have the same attributes. Mineral insulation of a greater density is needed for sound resistance than that offered by thermal insulation. Thermal insulation relies on soft and squidgy stuff inflated with air pockets to trap the heat in; sound relies on squashed and heavy stuff to add mass to the wall and keep airborne sound out.

New separating stud walls should always be built in cavity construction as a double stud frame wall, with at least a 240-mm cavity width. If that seems excessive, it is because that dimension is measured between the inner faces of plasterboard on both sides when using 100-mm deep timber studs. The distance between the studs themselves will reduce the cavity here to a mere 40 mm. Semi-rigid mineral wool insulation can then be installed between each stud, keeping this 40 mm as a clear void. Two layers of plasterboard on each face then cover it. The first layer is a 19-mm thick plank and the second a 12.5-mm sound-resistant plasterboard. With full attention to detail and good workmanship, constructions such as this should offer 45 decibels of airborne sound insulation, but the key to this is in the workmanship. Avoid making holes in the plasterboard for pipes or cables, and isolate the frame from the floor, ceiling and existing adjacent walls with a resilient strip beneath the timber. It does not matter that your head and sole plates will be fixed through it in this situation. Low-frequency sound can be transmitted around these peripheries, and these strips seem to cut out a few decibels at that level, which can make all the difference between passing and failing a sound test. For it to work properly, the strip must be wide enough to ensure the plasterboard touches it as well as the studwork plates; any excess width can be trimmed off after plastering.

How to support timber partitions

Although not load-bearing, these partitions have some dead weight of their own, and the floor structure needs to be capable of carrying them. They should be supported on double or treble joists if they run parallel with the wall, and you may need to add additional joists alongside the existing ones to achieve this directly beneath the sole plate. A resilient isolation strip should be used between the sole or head plates and the joists to separate the construction. Those extra joists need to sit on bearings before they can be capable of sharing the load. It is not enough to simply thicken the existing ones with them.

If the joists are running perpendicular, the support is available as long as the joists are not overstressed for the span. If they are deflecting already, adding extra weight will cause them to fail completely. Extra joists may be installed between them or alongside them to strengthen the floor structure.

Dry lining

If you are not finishing the wall with plaster, but using tapered edge plasterboard, filled and smoothed ready for decorating, then you are dry lining. Dry lining is plaster-free. That does not make it easy. The joints still have to be filled, and they are wider than you might imagine. Once filled, they have to be polished smooth before the filler sets hard if you do not want to resort to sanding them all down later because, with dry lining, the joints should be invisible once you have decorated. There is an art to this process, even though it may sound like a DIY dream.

Once the joints are finished, it is essential to use a primer on the wall first. Some decorators prefer to use a mist coat of emulsion, which is simply a watered-down first coat, but you will find that the primer sold by plasterboard manufacturers is easier

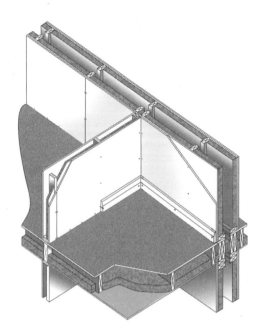

▸ Typical timber-frame construction with separating double-stud wall and single-stud internal walls.

to apply and more efficient at taking the absorption out of the surface. Trying to paint directly on to an untreated plasterboard sheet is like trying swim against the tide – hard work to say the least and not an economical use of energy or paint. Most of the latter will be soaked up rather than spread out. As well as making it easier to paint, the primer covers the joints and reduces the chance of them being seen through the finished paintwork, creating an even canvas on which to add your choice of colour. If you go with white, it is even more essential.

It is difficult to get a perfectly flat and smooth surface over filled joints. Given enough time and effort, working them down from what is usually a 3-mm fill to a finish that is as smooth as possible is achievable with the right tools (sponges and fine sanding paper). If you really want a consistently smooth finish, however, you should use a finishing plaster coat. It is amazing how shining a bright light at an angle across a wall surface reveals all its imperfections; this is the only way of judging how good the surface finish is.

Sound and windows

In 2003, the government was proposing to introduce soundproofing to the outside fabric of new homes. The standard was aimed at cutting down traffic noise and the like. It was dropped at the last minute and no requirements currently exist for external sound insulation. If they did, they would do well to look towards windows.

Windows are not all that good at cutting down noise. Indeed, they are often the weak point in the structure. If they have poorly fitting seals and thin glass, noise is easily transferred through them. Even a very thin gap around a bedroom window will allow an air leak that will not only keep your room chilled in winter, but also keep you awake at night to 24/7 life outside. Double glazing is good for sound insulation; triple glazing is even better. It is the sealed cavity between the two that provides the insulation.

Sound insulation works to the 'mass law', but glass is relatively thin and low in mass. Hence the problem with windows. Something else happens with sound, too, that is most unusual. As frequencies pass from low to high, the noise transmitted through a structure (like a window) actually becomes less. But then it all goes sadly wrong when the frequency reaches a certain level – known as the 'critical frequency' – because, when this is achieved, it is as though a hole opens up in the structure and sound pours through. In an odd way, double-glazing a single-glazed window is no help when this occurs because invariably both panes are the same thickness (usually 4 mm) and their symmetry allows the frequency peaks to superimpose on to each other, magnifying and strengthening. Normal laminated glass that has an inner core of plastic known as the PVB interlayer, bonding the two sheets together, does not seem to perform much better until that interlayer is changed for something with a sound-dampening quality to stop the vibration. Special laminated glass with an acoustic resin core is available as a sound-insulating product. This has the added security of not being easily smashed – instead, it merely cracks like a car windscreen when it is hit by a stone.

Broadly speaking, these sound-rated laminates cut out an extra six or seven decibels of noise over a conventional laminated glass pane. In a window that faces a road, railway or any other source of noise, that ability could make a most welcome difference. Using an acoustic laminate as the outer leaf of double glazing will help enormously, perhaps leaving ten or more decibels outside of your home compared to a standard double-glazed window.

Sound Testing

As the results of sound tests are independently certified, acoustic engineers have to be qualified and registered to carry them out. There are engineers trading who are not qualified and registered, and the results of their tests are unlikely to be accepted by building control. They should either be UKAS (United Kingdom Accreditation Service) accredited or a member of the ANC (Association of Noise Consultants).

Robust Standard Detail System

Set up in 2004 for new house builders who did not like the idea of sound tests, the Robust Standard Detail System works a bit like joining a club. You pay a fee and you get the catalogue of approved details from which to choose one that suits you and your situation when it comes to sound insulation. You then register that detail with the scheme and the building control authority and stick to that detail religiously. Any variation or deviation from that detail, no matter how slight, invalidates it.

A Robust Standard Detail can be adopted, but these details were designed exclusively for new build when they were introduced in 2005 and offer no guarantee of passing acoustic tests. The system has not been available to anyone dividing homes or converting them, only to new home builders, which means that any home division or conversion will still have to be sound tested at pre-completion stage.

When measuring sound insulation, acoustic engineers are seeking to see how much noise has been cut out, and to do this we have to know how much is produced in the first instance. Noise can be divided into two types based on how it travels: airborne and impact. The terms speak for themselves. Airborne nose is those waves of pressure in the atmosphere, and impact noise travels as vibrations through solid matter after a collision. The resistance to both forms must be tested in floors, but only airborne testing is done for walls.

Airborne sound testing uses 'pink' noise played from a CD. Pink noise is a roar of interference, amplified until it sounds a bit like a 747 on take-off, played out through multifaceted loudspeakers into a room on one side of the separating structure. This room is known as the source room and is a bad place to be without headphones. A handheld meter can then record the noise level in this room and in a receiver room on the other side of the separating construction, measuring just how effective the sound insulation is. A number of meter readings are usually taken from different spots around the receiver room to work out an average measurement across the sound field.

Although the loudness of sound is the main consideration, we cannot ignore the frequency content of it. Frequency is measured in hertz (cycles per second), as the rate at which a sound wave fluctuates. Frequencies are detectable not only at differing levels by differing species, but also, it seems, by differing age groups. Adolescents are said to be capable of hearing higher pitched

Performance standards

To meet Building Regulation standards, a minimum level for airborne sound and a maximum level for impact sound must be met when new dwellings are being formed by a 'material change of use' (as defined by the Building Regulations):

FLOORS AND WALLS	airborne sound	minimum 43 decibels
FLOORS	impact sound	maximum 64 decibels

Note: standards taken from the 2003 edition of Approved Document E

frequencies than older adults – you might want to remember that if you own a dog whistle.

Failing sound tests

Without question, the greatest fear among home dividers is the failed sound test. Spending money to install a system of acoustic insulation in the first instance and not being able to test it until the place is finished, to find out whether it is OK or not, is a bit on the nerve-jangling side. For most sound test that I have witnessed, the results have proved positive – but not all of them. Following a recognised system of insulation is always going to help, but it is not a guarantee of passing. The reason for the uncertainty lies in the quality of workmanship employed in installing the sound insulation and also in the fabric and design of the existing building. Both of these factors can be extremely variable.

One acoustic engineering company has reported about 5 per cent of tests failing in conversion work. The reasons for these failures included using the wrong blocks in separating walls, bridging of the cavities in cavity walls with joists running through and mortar droppings, poor sealing of gaps in the construction of both floors and walls, and flanking transmission problems.

Chimneys, pipes and spotlights – three ways to fail
Holes in the construction will not help you to pass a sound test or an inspection, but at times holes have to be made. For soil pipes, you may have fitted an intumescent collar, but that will not help to stop the noise. Only by boxing it in, surrounded with mineral wool and cladding, will you be able to kill the sound path made by the thin plastic pipe.

Extractor fans may have to be ducted from internal bathrooms or kitchens out to the external walls. Using the floor void to hide the duct pipe has always been a smart move, but not when it is a separating floor. In a kitchen, there is probably no quicker way to spread a fire than to use the ducting to bypass the ceiling and pull the smoke and heat through to the floor above. A suspended ceiling that is independent might allow you to do this by passing through the void, but an under-drawn ceiling will not be so forgiving.

Chimneys can be easier to solve by bricking up a fireplace and lining over it. Trying to maintain them as working fires when the flue links to the apartment above, will be disastrous for both fire spread and sound.

Recessed spotlights are, I think, a much greater threat to fire resistance than sound, and if I could persuade you not to use recessed spotlights in your ceilings I would, but I am painfully aware that many people still find them hugely appealing. Apart from anything else, the light they provide is often hugely excessive to the needs of the situation. If you must have recessed spotlights, bear in mind that making a hole in the ceiling to fit them damages both fire-resistance and sound insulation, and you will need to fit special covers to the backs of them. Usually they come in the form of hoods or cover boxes that both insulate the surrounding structure from noise and fire passing through the holes and avoid the light itself overheating. Dichroic recessed lights throw a huge amount of heat backwards to avoid the lamp itself from overheating and blowing. This kickback of heat is a problem and the reason why it is best to avoid recessed lamps in dividing floors altogether. The only time it appears safe to install them is when you have built an independent ceiling below that effectively has a cavity between it and the ceiling above, or when you have purchased a specialist fitting with built-in protection.

Flanking sound transmission

Sound, as we have begun to realise, behaves in strange ways. It can vibrate through the fabric of your home by sneaking around a sound-lagged floor and down the walls. That is to say *through* the walls, using them as a pathway between floors. This surprising ability means that flanking transmission, as it is known, cannot be ignored. Mass in walls counts for a lot, but so does isolating the finishes from too much contact with the wall.

Older properties built with solid brick walls fare much better than newer ones built with soft thermal block walls. Inevitably, the modern home has a cavity wall with an inner skin made from soft aerated blocks, and they seem to transfer sound quite efficiently. If you have this kind of construction to deal with, it pays to line the walls internally with sound-rated plasterboard that is isolated from the wall itself. To achieve this, a timber or metal stud dry-lining system can be erected between floor and ceiling, keeping a small gap between the studs and the wall. This air gap will prove invaluable if the wall behaves like a tuning fork and starts to vibrate with sound. The effect may not be noticeable to your ears, but a sound meter can show up a dramatic increase in the decibels when held near a wall compared to levels in the centre of a room.

Overcoming failed tests

Aside from abandoning the project, failing a sound test means improving the floor with remedial treatment and retaking the test. Hopefully, your sound testing engineer will be able to advise you on why the test has failed and on ways of making up the shortfall. It may be easier than you think.

Home dividers looking at these materials cannot help but think that they will stick down a deep-pile carpet with a gel backing and a decent bit of underlay – job done. And to some extent they would be right. Carpet is a great acoustic insulant, but unfortunately it is a soft furnishing and not an element of the structure. It can be replaced at the drop of a hat by the residents in favour of laminate or wood flooring that has no sound insulation qualities at all. I have lost count of the times when it has been suggested to me that, once the carpet is laid, the floor will be much better. Sound testing has to be done before carpets are laid and for good reason. Carpet is excellent for cutting down noise, particularly deep-pile carpets with quality underlays. Indeed some underlay is labelled and named as sound absorbent. Unfortunately, carpet is not considered to be part of the fabric of a building. Instead it falls in the decorative finishing category, along with wallpaper, laminate flooring and other furnishings.

There is an exception. An underlay material that is fully bonded down, fixed permanently, is acceptable, and there is such a thing as acoustic underlay. Glorified carpet underlay it may be because it is designed to be laid quickly and cleanly with the minimum of disruption, but as part of the floor structure and a valid means of achieving sound insulation it is bonded down permanently. Acrylic adhesives are often used to achieve this. The sheet products may be anything up to 20 mm thick depending on what level of sound reduction you are trying to achieve. Some are much thinner, but all tend to be highly dense and weighty. Some come in panels that have to be laid in brick bond format with the joints staggered,

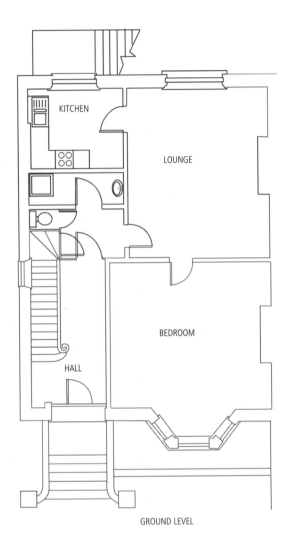

▸ The stacking principle of layout design is shown here (and opposite) with bedrooms, lounges and kitchens above each other, to reduce noise nuisance.

KITCHEN

LOUNGE

BEDROOM

HALL

GROUND LEVEL

and for these to work the floor must be level to ensure that there are no gaps between the panels and they all butt tightly together. It is not always easy to discover what they are made of because the marketing gets in the way with descriptions such as 'soundproof high-density elastomeric resilient matting', which simply means it is quite heavy yet stretchy stuff that has been cut up into manageable sheets. Of those that I have seen, some have been made from the rubber of recycled car tyres and others of dense foam, but all are generally prone to puncturing and require a rigid floor finish over the top to protect and cover them. This could simply be sheets of MDF board or plywood only 6 mm thick, but it should be enough to spread the load out from the feet of furniture that would otherwise damage it.

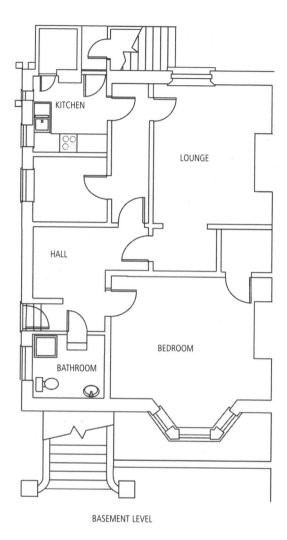

BASEMENT LEVEL

One tricky bit of detailing is the perimeter, and this is another area where your sound testing can fail. To deal with the problem of flanking transmission, the insulation must either be stopped short of the wall or dressed up it behind the skirting boards. Stopping short allows for carpet gripper to be fitted without puncturing the material. Depending on the product, you might be able to reduce both the airborne and impact sound transmission by as much as seven or eight decibels with these alone in a typical timber floor.

The same material is also available in strips that are stuck down (some are self-adhesive) to the tops of the joists before the timber boards are rested back down. Obviously in an older home this can result in a floor that resembles the surface of the sea to

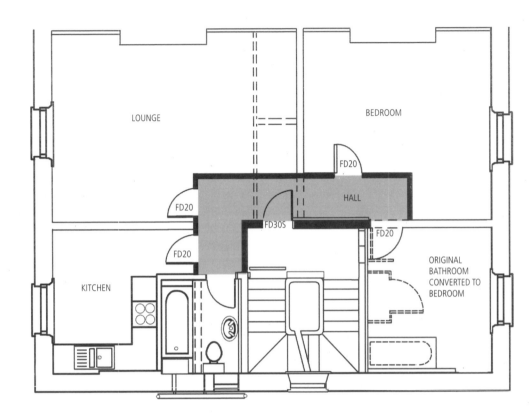

LOUNGE

BEDROOM

FD20

FD20

HALL

FD30S

FD20

FD20

ORIGINAL
BATHROOM
CONVERTED TO
BEDROOM

KITCHEN

▲ On this floor plan, a hallway has been formed inside the apartment to create the two-door fire protection to the stairs.

walk across. The boards cannot be fixed down because the fixings would transmit the sound through them. People have sometimes been driven to fixing battens between the joists to secure the boards, too, but that defeats the object. It is a bit of a weird arrangement when the battens are small (50 mm square, perhaps) and wholly incapable of taking any weight. Rather, it acts as a fixing point for your boards (which without it would have taken on the behaviour of a bouncy castle), but it still creates a solid sound path – the very thing the product was trying to avoid. I have seen people struggle with these materials and end up screwing the boards down through the insulation as well, but they can be used in situations where the joists are level and the floor structure is true and even – in other words, in a relatively modern home.

Dividing against fire

When fire breaks out in a home it is often undetected in the early stages. Unfortunately, what happens next happens fast – smoke and toxic gases rise up from the source of the fire and spread out across the ceiling. The smokes and gas, as much as the flames, quickly heat the air in the room, and this current of hot air forces the lethal mixture down the walls in a curtain that can soon block the exit doors. In a few minutes, the air inside the room has been superheated to the point where furnishings and furniture can spontaneously combust – literally burst into flames. This combustion event is known as a 'flashover', and firefighters the world over dread it. At this point, being inside the room would mean sudden death because, for a flashover to occur, the room temperature has reached between 1000°C and 1500°C. In most cases, the descending cloud of toxic gas and smoke kills anyone it comes into contact with, long before a flashover occurs. As a result, much of the fire precautions required in dividing homes are aimed at keeping smoke out of the hall and stairway, and leaving a clear passage of escape.

Designing for fire safety

As it happens, divided homes are inherently safer from fire than single-family dwellings. Dividing a building into separated dwellings is a process known as 'compartmentation'. Making boxes with fire-resisting construction restricts the spread of fire from one part of the building to another, and that, in a crude definition, is what apartments are.

Where they become less safe is when they offer only one way out. One staircase/exit door is a common situation in small apartment buildings, but it can still be a safe one. Instead of the entrance door of each apartment leading directly to the accommodation, whether it be the kitchen or the lounge or any other room, it should lead to an inner lobby. As small as it may be, this hallway creates a safety valve, with separate doors leading to the rooms themselves. In this arrangement, a fire in any room but the lobby itself has to bypass two doors before it reaches the common stairway or hall. That extra door can be proved invaluable, but like the front door is has to be capable of holding up a fire.

Fire alarms

Separating construction does a good job in reducing fire spread and protecting escape routes, but what saves lives is early warnings. Early warning of a fire is essential, and all buildings should now have fire alarms of some description. We are now used to the smoke detector and alarm units that are known as the stand-alone type in our homes. They provide both the detector and sounder in one unit. Using mains-powered versions of these is now required, and these have the benefit of being capable of interlinking with each other on a circuit. The more parts of the building covered by them, the greater the protection. For larger circuits, though, it is traditional to have separated parts of the system – detectors, manual call points, sounders – in specific locations, and they are usually linked by a control board positioned near the main entrance.

Types of fire alarm system

For buildings divided into apartments or maisonettes, the usual approach has been to either provide an L1 or L2 system comprising of smoke and heat detectors in appropriate locations, both inside the divided homes and in the common areas and escape routes. Faced with the false alarm problems with these systems caused by one occupant repeatedly burning his toast and resulting in the entire building being evacuated, it may be possible to agree something else. A circuit of smoke and heat alarm/detectors in each divided home would be interlinked to give warning to that occupant without setting off a general alarm in the common parts that would evacuate the building. In these parts, a separate circuit of smoke detectors and manual call points can be used to raise the general alarm.

Manual call points are needed so that residents escaping a fire in their flat (for example) can raise the alarm and warn others in the building when they do need to evacuate and before smoke has penetrated the escape routes. They come in two types: A and B. A types sound when the glass is broken and keep on ringing the alarm once activated. B types can and tend to be used in shops where they want to exercise additional controls over false alarms and people departing hastily, and these need an additional operation after the glass is broken.

Coverage inside divided homes

A single smoke alarm in the entrance lobby or hall (on each floor) used to be acceptable. Clearly that is a bit inadequate, as most fires occur in kitchens and other rooms. Additional coverage in these rooms should now be provided. With kitchens that means a heat detector, to avoid those toasting incidents. Heat detectors work on a rise in temperature and are not activated by smoke unless it is heating up, as it will do in a fire situation.

Coverage on escape routes

The manual call points should be located outside of each entrance door, plus one close to the final (common) exit door. Leaving the building should not mean having to go looking for the call points first. The zone panel should also be located here so that arriving firefighters can see which detector has been triggered and where the origins of the fire are. A fire alarm layout plan of the ground floor can also be located in a fireproof box at this point.

Fire doors

There is something about fire doors that people do not like. It is not really their appearance because many are faced and designed to look no different than an ordinary internal door. It is not the weight of them. On the whole, they are a little heavier, but most people consider a little robustness to be a good thing in a door – it implies quality and is good for security. No, it is the fact that they are fitted with self-closing mechanisms. Traditionally they always have been, and few people appreciate a door in their home that refuses to stay open. Combined with the fact that self-closers need to close a door with enough force to latch it shut, they can prove to be a threat to slow or small fingers.

In 2007, the requirement for self-closing devices inside dwellings was removed (except for internal doors to garages), but this exemption does not apply to entrance doors to homes that are located in common stairways or halls; these still need self-closers. A door that is not shut, however, is no use in a fire; doors that are shut, especially fire-rated doors, buy you valuable time if a fire occurs. Time to escape, or time for rescue. When a fire takes hold, smoke can spread rapidly through a home with open doors and nothing to slow its progress.

L SYSTEMS FOR PROTECTION OF LIFE

L1 Installed throughout the building
L2 Installed in defined parts of the building (and usually in the parts covered by an L3 system)
L3 Systems sounding a warning to all areas of the building except those in the room where the fire has originated
L4 Systems installed to protect corridors, stairways and halls as the escape route and circulation areas
L5 Systems not described above that have been installed to protect designated areas and have a specified objective in so doing

P SYSTEMS FOR PROPERTY PROTECTION
These are not applicable to homes unless they are supplementary to L systems. For reference, they are either P1 (installed throughout the building) or P2 (installed in defined areas of the building).

SMOKE ALARM (ROOMS AND HALLWAYS)

HEAT ALARM (KITCHENS AND GARAGES)

▸ Fire alarms should be mains-powered and interlinked by cabling or wireless systems to activate each other or general sounders upon detection of the hazard.

Fire door keep shut

Keep locked shut

Automatic fire door keep clear

▲ Fire-door signs are essential in the common parts of the building.

Types of fire door

FD30 A fire door with 30 minutes' integrity and 30 minutes' insulation from heat, complete with intumescent (expanding) seals fitted to the frame surrounding its three edges. Also known as a 30/30 door.

FD20 As above, but with 20 minutes integrity and insulation. Can be used without self-closers as internal doors to rooms.

FD30 S As an FD30, but with one extra feature – smoke seals that appear as brushes incorporated within tumescent seals, which appear like draught excluders. Their job is to keep out cold smoke. It is smoke that often kills people before they awake, overcoming them with toxic fumes. A rubber-strip type is also available, but these have a tendency to wear, making them less effective. Brushes are far better.

FD60S As an FD30S, but with 60 minutes' integrity and insulation, making a 60/60 door. Usually the frame structure is much stronger than with FD30 doors.

SC Self-closing device fitted in compliance with BS:6459: Door Closers.

VP Glazed Vision Panel included in the door leaf, with fire-resisting glass rated to the period of fire-resistance of the door itself. Vision panels are rarely installed in domestic doors where there is a need for privacy.

Fire door or fire exit door?

It is easy to confuse fire doors with fire exit doors. The term 'fire door' is a confusing abbreviation of 'fire-rated door' or 'fire-resisting door', both of which are far more descriptive of what the door does. It holds back fire, acting to keep fire from spreading from one part of a building to another. Fire exit doors, on the other hand, are generally not fire-resistant. They are the emergency exit from a building, bedecked with panic bars and exit signage. As they are the last portal to clear to get out of the place (unless the fire is outside), making them fire-resistant would not really help. What matters with a fire exit door is that it is open, or openable, within an instant and without a key.

Apart from stronger ironmongery (with a higher melting point), there are no other discernible features of a fire door. Indeed, they are made to blend in with ordinary internal doors, with the one difference being extra weight from their more solid construction.

All fire and fire exit doors should open outwards, in the direction of travel. In the case of dwellings where the number of people using them is minimal, this is less important and you should hang them whichever way works best for ease of use and given the space you have available. The common entrance door is best provided with a latch that requires a key to enter but not to leave. Opening it to get out should be something you can do with your thumb in a single action.

Lobbies

The protective lobby is an important part of apartment buildings where a common stair or hallway provides the access to several individual apartments. If that stair or hallway is the only way out of the building, it is important to ensure that it will not become compromised by smoke or fire to the point that it is unusable in an emergency. In other words, if fire occurs in a lower floor apartment and the occupants leave, the last thing the people upstairs need is the fire breaking out into the stairway, preventing them from escaping.

Single escape routes are precious and have to be looked after with fire precautions that are built into the design, and the most basic of those is the apartment lobby (a.k.a. inner hallway). The lobby creates a safety valve of two-door separation between the common escape route and the habitable rooms. Fire-resistant doors are fitted to the apartment entrance (FD30S) and each of the rooms (FD20) that lead off the apartment's lobby. There is always a temptation, particularly with small apartments such as studio flats, to have just the one door and skip the lobby, which would take up valuable space, but that would compromise the fire escape route and is likely to be unacceptable to your building control authority.

▾ Fire-protected steel beams encased in plasterboard.

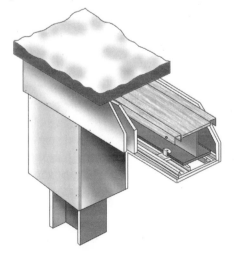

Unless, of course, you have something better, something that will extinguish the fire automatically before it has hardly begun.

Sprinklers

When we hear the word 'S' word, the sight of the lawn going brown in summer might spring to mind first, rapidly followed by a scene from a movie of our hero setting off the sprinkler system with his lighter, to flood the building with water and dampen a hostage crisis. Neither of these is helpful.

We strive to keep water out of our homes by keeping a decent roof over our head and making sure that the bath does not overflow, so the thought of deliberately flooding it is hard to conceive. As it happens, sprinklers are not so easily activated. When they are, they are quite conservative about water use.

Although they are only just beginning to appear in homes, sprinklers in other buildings such as hotels have been around since the 1870s and are a practical and valued form of fire protection. It seems a dangerous fact to quote, but their record of protecting people in fires is unsurpassed and no lives have been lost to fire in dwellings where a sprinkler system has been installed. Sprinklers

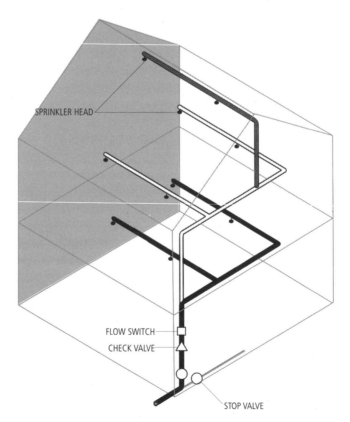

▸ Typical layout plan for a sprinkler system. Note: the flow switch will be wired to trigger the fire alarm.

SPRINKLER HEAD

FLOW SWITCH

CHECK VALVE

STOP VALVE

are designed to tackle a fire in the early stages before it has had a chance to take hold and spread. They buy you extra time to escape from the building and, in most cases, extinguish a fire completely long before the fire brigade has turned up. Smoke alarms can only tell us when our lives are at risk and, from time to time, sadly lives are lost with the smoke alarm still sounding.

Smoke can still be an issue, but it should be reduced in volume and your chances of surviving in a home on fire are said to be about 47 per cent better when sprinklers alone are fitted. If you have both smoke alarms and a sprinkler system, that survival rate jumps to 97 per cent. In a nutshell, people do not tend to perish in fires at home with protection such as this in place.

The detector heads of sprinklers are designed to activate on a rise in temperature, not on contact with smoke, and consequently they do not go off accidentally. Statistically, they are said to have only a one in 16 million chance of going off accidentally, although I am not entirely sure how they came up with this figure. When a head is activated, only that one sprinkler is triggered, not all of them. Consequently, it is not possible to flood the whole building and rescue the hostages by doing this. Each sprinkler head has its own control sensor to detect a fire growth beneath it and it alone.

As you can imagine the design of sprinkler systems has a lot to do with water pressure, and that can be a bit of a problem. Hotels and superstores tend to have their own massive water tanks to provide the water their sprinklers will need, but most domestic systems rely on the mains. The company that delivers your water may not be able to guarantee high pressure, but it is usually good enough for low-rise buildings. It is the large and tall properties that struggle with pressure. The legal minimum pressure that water suppliers have to provide us with is often inadequate for a large multi-storey building. As water climbs up through the vertical riser and travels along the distribution pipes, it loses pressure. If the pressure was poor to start with, the chances are that, when it finally reaches the sprinkler head, it will emerge as a slight dribble rather than a fire-dousing spray.

At least half a bar of pressure is required at the head of the run for it to function properly. A sprinkler system in full flow must deliver at least 60 litres of water per minute. This may seem a lot, but is in fact far less water than the fire brigade releases when it turns up. In that respect, sprinklers can be considered as a way of saving both your property and your life. Fire service hoses tend to deliver around 900 litres of water per minute by comparison, and can flood a building and its contents very quickly. It will help

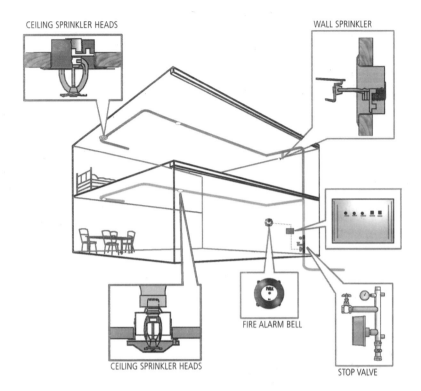

CEILING SPRINKLER HEADS

WALL SPRINKLER

FIRE ALARM BELL

CEILING SPRINKLER HEADS

STOP VALVE

▸ Sprinklers, when installed, can be activated to trip a flow switch and sound the fire alarm

enormously if the fire is out before the fire brigade arrives. All that then remains to do is to turn off the water supply at the stopcock to shut the system down.

If that still seems too much to bear, you might consider using mist instead of water.

Water or Mist?

An alternative type of sprinkler system is known as the 'water mist system'. Instead of an actual fine spray of water, a vapour cloud of mist that saturates the air is released from the sprinkler head. Water mist systems are in use around the world, and, as they discharge less water over your property in a fire, they are well thought of. The British Standard for sprinklers (BS:

PERFORMANCE REQUIREMENTS FOR DOMESTIC SPRINKLERS	
Minimum operating pressure at the sprinkler head	0.5 bar
Typical design flow rate	60 L/min
Design maximum number of heads operating	2
Maximum design flow rate	84 L/min

Pressure testing

A sprinkler system should be less prone to leaks than your central heating system. Although the plastic pipework is charged to a similar pressure in use as that of an unvented heating system and hot-water system, sprinkler systems are pressure tested on installation to three times that pressure.

9251:2005) introduced in 2005, however, sets a minimum flow rate of 60 litres per minute over an area of 15 square metres. The density of the water falling thus translates to about 4 mm per minute. In other words, in one minute, your carpet should have a 4 mm depth of water on it. Mist systems do not use half as much water (less than 2 mm over the same area) and therefore fall outside the standard. In fact, they work by raising the humidity dramatically to saturation point and starving a fire of oxygen, rather than dousing it as such. Sprinklers tend to soak the walls to prevent fire growth over them; mist systems do not. Consequently, in 2007, at the advent of this new form of fire protection, they find themselves a little out of the market. This is a shame, as they may prove easier for people to live with.

▾ The sequence of sprinkler head activation, showing the glass vial shattering to release the plug and the water flow.

Appearance

As with fire doors, we do not actually want to see fire precautions in our homes. We simply need to know that they are there. Back in 1990, when smoke alarms first came into mandatory use in new homes, the biggest resistance to them came about because of their appearance. Few of us appreciated having ugly grill-faced plastic boxes surface fixed to our new and nicely decorated ceilings. Worse still, the budget ones soon turned from white to yellow when exposed to UV light because of the cheap plastic from which they were made. Smoke alarms have improved slightly, but mostly what has

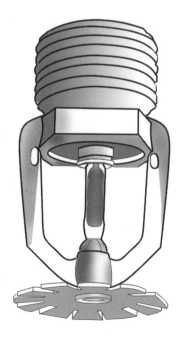

happened is that we have become use to seeing them, and it has been a long long time now since I heard anybody complain about having to fit them.

Sprinklers in their raw form look worse than smoke alarms, but thankfully that is not an issue because they are concealed from view when the installation is complete. The pipework, which tends to be orange, is located above the ceiling structure and only the sprinkler heads emerge. All that you see on the ceiling, however, is a smooth plain white disc of plastic seated close to the ceiling finish. These discs are sacrificial covers that drop away in contact with fire, and they do a wonderful job of hiding the metal deflector and vial. If only smoke detectors could be this invisible.

How sprinklers are activated

Sprinklers are not activated by smoke, but by heat. If you irritated one sprinkler with a naked flame held beneath it, that one sprinkler would release a spray of water, but the others would remain inactive. Each sprinkler has its own trigger mechanism which, in most cases, consists of a glass vial filled with a glycerine-based liquid that expands when heated. An air bubble exists within the solution to accommodate some normal expansion, but, when the liquid is heated by fire, rapid expansion occurs at a certain temperature (typically 155°C). The glass then shatters and the plug that holds back the pressurised water is released.

The glass vial can be made even thinner for a quicker response to the expanding liquid, but most are designed to activate somewhere between 60 and 90 seconds after the heat has been applied. The plug that the vial was holding in place is pushed away instantly by the water pressure in the system, deflecting out of the way by a bevelled edge. The underside of the detector has a cog-like deflector plate for the jet of water to hit and create the spray. Some sprinkler models have a metal plate trigger instead. A solder holds two spring-loaded plates together until, in the heat of a fire, the solder melts, the plates spring apart and the plug is released. These semi-mechanical actions mean that systems with metal-plate triggers do need some maintenance over their lifetime, but with it they are expected to last for at least 50 years.

As already noted, even the smoke from a smouldering fire acts like a heat engine, steadily increasing the air temperature in the room. With the hot air fanning out over the ceiling, any sprinkler head it comes into contact with (the nearest one to the seat of the fire) will be activated. In most cases, that one sprinkler head will extinguish the fire before it spreads any further. Usually it will cool the surrounding air with the spray of water, preventing other

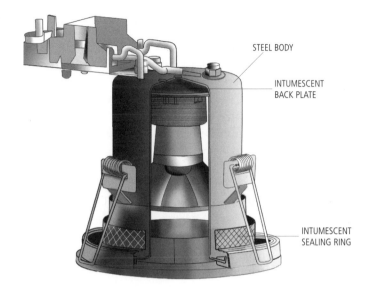

STEEL BODY

INTUMESCENT
BACK PLATE

INTUMESCENT
SEALING RING

◄ Recessed
spotlights
require
protective
hoods or built-
in intumescent
seals (exploded
view).

sprinkler heads from activating and dousing the fire until
somebody turns the water off at the control valve. By the time the
fire brigade arrives, the fire is likely to be out.

Although sprinkler systems are not required by Building
Regulations, they can be used to trade off other requirements
which cannot be met, giving greater flexibility to the design and
layout of your divided homes.

Fire resistance in dividing homes

Generally speaking, 60 minutes of fire resistance has been
required to separate one home from another for many years now.
Fire spread requirements were first introduced after the Great Fire
of London in 1666, which showed how easy it is to destroy lots
of buildings when they are close together. Although a relaxation
to 30 minutes was introduced for apartment and maisonette
conversions, the current sound insulation requirements can be
used to help achieve 60 if you work from below on the ceilings.
This is yet another advantage of using this method as opposed to
working from the floors above. Still, 30 minutes can be easily
achieved by one layer of the right fire-rated plasterboard beneath
whatever ceiling exists at present. It is then more a case of limiting
the number of holes you make in it for plumbing and lighting.

Heat is an unfortunate by-product of many modern lamps.
Halogen and dichroic reflector lamps produce a lot of it and need
placing at a suitable distance from their subject. I have lost count
of the number of times I have burnt my fingers on metal light

A sprinkler test demonstration

On a bright but breezy spring day, I joined a group of building inspectors and fire safety officers on a housing estate in Kent to set fire to two bungalows. The media were also there to watch the demonstration. After an introductory talk on the benefits of sprinklers, we were all transported to the test site to look around the pair of identical semi-detached bungalows before they were set alight. Having seen inside both and witnessed the similar furnishings and décor, we retired to a nearby marquee to watch the show. The fires were to be started in the lounge rooms, in an armchair. So that we could see exactly what was happening, fire-protected cameras were locked off inside the rooms to feed video direct to large-screen televisions in our marquee. The bungalow on the right had a sprinkler system installed; the one on the left did not. They both had smoke alarms. The fires were lit simultaneously in each bungalow, and very soon smoke started to emerge from the windows of both. You could see, however, that the single sprinkler that soon burst into life had extinguished the flames in the right-hand property. The firefighting team moved forward and quickly put the other fire out, which had only just started to take hold.

Once the front door of each bungalow was opened, the smoke poured out from both in equal volumes, although there may have been some steam mixed in among it with the sprinklered bungalow. Nonetheless, it was a successful demonstration of how quickly sprinkler systems can deal with a fire (quicker than the fire brigade's standard response time). I imagine that, if the firefighters had left it longer before breaking in, the sprinkler would have saturated out much of the smoke as well. We were invited to reinspect the lounge rooms of each bungalow and, in one bungalow, apart from a soggy carpet, it was remarkable how little damage had occurred. Much of the possessions were intact.

In the other bungalow, sans sprinklers, the walls were black and most of the room's contents were destroyed – television, videos, books and pictures, along with the furniture, were all molten or charred. Interestingly enough, drooping down on the ceiling like a plastic stalactite, grossly disfigured by the heat of the fire, the remains of the smoke alarm continued to beep away like a superhero. Smoke alarms, it seems, are incredibly resilient, but if you do not hear them and leave pronto, they will not save your life like a sprinkler.

fittings with these lamps in them. Contact burns from light fittings never get a mention in the news, compared to scalding water and thermostatic taps, but it seems to me that they are just as bad. I often see wall lights that are practically red hot placed well within in a child's reach.

In this instance, where we are considering how ceilings provide fire-resistance to upper floors, cutting out an array of holes in them for recessed spotlights does not do much to maintain that

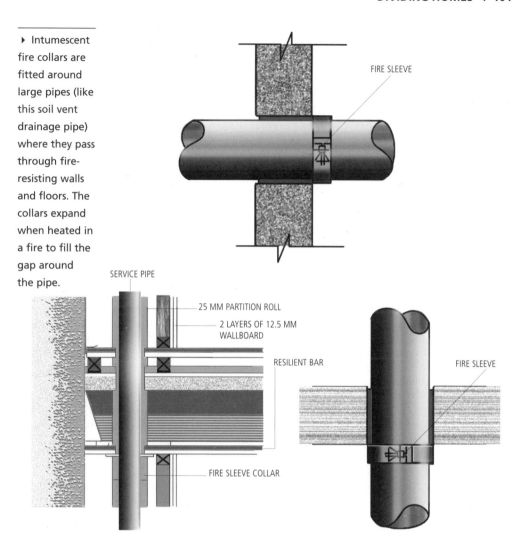

▸ Intumescent fire collars are fitted around large pipes (like this soil vent drainage pipe) where they pass through fire-resisting walls and floors. The collars expand when heated in a fire to fill the gap around the pipe.

FIRE SLEEVE

SERVICE PIPE

25 MM PARTITION ROLL

2 LAYERS OF 12.5 MM WALLBOARD

RESILIENT BAR

FIRE SLEEVE

FIRE SLEEVE COLLAR

fire resistance. The lights themselves can be very hot in operation and much of that heat is displaced through the back of the unit. Dichroic lamps throw some of the heat backwards through the glass and should not be fitted in ceilings without fire-protective covers. The problem of puncturing the integrity of a fire-rated ceiling has been resolved with hoods that fit over the back of the unit. Somewhat awkward to fit, these material jackets fit loosely into the hole for the recessed light fitting to occupy. The fireproof material reduces the risk of the unit or indeed the hole causing or allowing fire to spread. Expanding foam insulation does not do the same; it blackens and burns instead.

Thankfully the manufacturers of these types of lights have now realised that it is better to manufacture a fire-rated light fitting in the first place. These fire-rated units have an intumescent material neck around the circumference of the housing where it pushes into the hole in the plasterboard ceiling. In a fire condition, the material expands to seal the gap between it and the hole more effectively against smoke and flame. In addition, a circular disc of intumescent material is located in the cap of the downlighter behind the lamp itself, to seal the back of the fitting in the same way. These lights tend to be more robustly made from steel and ceramic, but all this quality pays off with improved sound and fire resistance – both elements you are trying to protect.

Intumescent fire collars can be fitted to the soil pipes that pass through fire-resisting walls and ceilings, but as these do nothing for sound insulation or the interior décor they are usually boxed in and lined with plasterboard layers to form a duct that can be decorated.

Fire retarding and intumescent coatings

The range of fire-retarding and intumescent products only continues to swell. There are fire-resisting paints, varnishes, sponges, strips, seals and even wallpapers on the market. At times you have little choice but to use them, but do so with extreme caution. Not only has the testing and advertised performance of some of these products been questioned, but there are those that are made with chemicals that you probably would not want sealed in to your airtight home today.

Intumescent products work by using the heat from a fire to trigger a chemical reaction that exudes from the treated product, engulfing and sealing it, and thus protecting it from fire. In the process, the product, whether it be a door or a sheet of glass, becomes unusable and will have to be disposed of. Other fire-retarding products simply seek to limit the spread of fire across them, as retardants. Most of the chemicals used as coatings are high in VOCs (volatile organic compounds) that not only emit gas during application, but also for some time afterwards. PBDEs (polybrominated diphenyl ethers) have been used excessively as fire retardants since the late 1970s, and are now present in quite high quantities in our bodies. Although the effect on humans is still unknown, laboratory animals subjected to high levels of PBDEs are said to have suffered from developmental problems related to learning, memory and behaviour. They have also exhibited thyroid problems in some instances.

Manufacturers are not shy to sell their products as 'necessary to meet the Building Regulations' where they are not or where more natural solutions are available. Many of them have limitations of use that are not clearly divulged to the consumer. For example, most intumescing coatings for wood are species-specific and have a disastrous effect on other species. Most seem to turn cherry wood bright orange, maple bright pink and any timber used outside white, soon after application – irreversible side effects. The lesson is to do your research and line up the facts to back up any manufacturer's claims before making your decisions.

Refuse spaces in common areas

Finding space for waste is always a problem, but now we are recycling more of it we need more space to store it until it can be collected. Home divisions only serve to magnify this problem. Whenever possible, refuse stores need to be kept outside of the building. The front garden is ideal if the store can be concealed and made acceptable to the planning authority, as it from here that the waste is collected. This is not so easy, though, when the front door is on the street or at the back edge of the footpath, or when a flight of steps stretches from the footpath up to the door. In these cases, it is often necessary to create a refuse store inside the building. It can be done if the structure surrounding it separates it from the building's escape route and has at least 60 minutes' fire resistance. It also needs to be fitted with an FD60S door if the door is internal to the common parts of the building, as well as fire-protected by sprinklers or smoke alarms. Generally speaking, as refuse stores represent an unacceptably high fire risk, access to them should not be via escape routes. This should always be a last resort only.

Refuse chutes can be built into high-rise buildings (over four storeys), but they are not necessary in low-rise ones. Not only do you have to find the space to install and fire-protect them, but also they create an unwelcome maintenance problem, will still probably represent a high fire risk and will introduce smells to the building that are less than pleasant.

It is not just the rooms and dividing structures that need to be resolved; supplying the new homes with all the services needed to support the occupants cannot be left until the end. This issue, too, needs to be addressed from the start.

CHAPTER 4

For most home dividers looking at creating a family annexe, separating the services from the rest of the home is unnecessary. They can simply be extended and the bills divided up between occupants. All that changes, however, when you create a new dwelling. Dividing homes into two or more dwellings means dividing services, and there are plenty of things to consider.

Gas and electricity

Getting connected

It is usually possible to arrange for a new gas or electricity connection through your supplier. The suppliers of both gas and electricity are licensed and, as I am sure you know, operate in a fully competitive market – meaning that you can chop and change who you buy the stuff from on a whim. Alas, these companies are acting only as merchants. They do not own, control or distribute these fuels – and consequently they are not the ones that authorise new connections. Regional transporters, as the network owners, do that, and it is their services that you require.

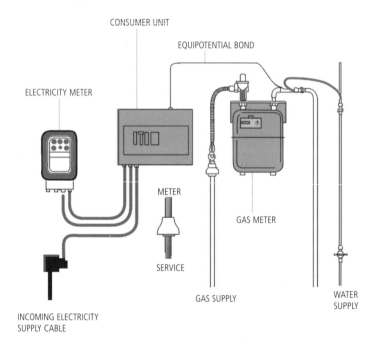

▲ Services equipment.

Unfortunately, new connections to gas and electricity supplies come with some bureaucracy and expense attached because, although the gas and electricity itself can be bought from various companies all competing with each other for your business, the actual work of connecting your new homes to the grid cannot. For that, you have no choice but to go to the infrastructure company that owns and maintains the distribution of these fuels. The National Grid plc may be the sole producer of gas and electricity but distributing them is another job. In 2007 there were five gas-network owners serving the regions and three companies licensed in the transmission of electricity. As distributors they are responsible for making connections to new homes. There may be many more supply companies, however, from which you can buy your gas or electricity, but only the distributors can get you connected to receive it. Previously known collectively as 'statutory undertakers', these distributors have the monopoly when it comes to getting you connected, and their charges and service illustrate this. Each one offers a procedure to follow that usually consumes time, so you need to embark on it at an early stage.

Dividing up a home will require splitting up an existing connection into one for each dwelling and installing individual meters housed in meter boxes. Some groundwork is likely, with new cable or pipework laid in excavated trenches, and you will be astonished to learn that only the suppliers are able to execute this work and that they charge for it. To find out how much these services will cost is a procedure in itself. Application forms are filled out and submitted for quotation, surveyors may visit the site and weeks, indeed months, may pass before you receive your quote. With flats and maisonettes on upper-floor levels, site surveys are usually carried out at least by the gas company, before a quote on the work is given. They tend not to quote for these 'off-plan'.

Once you have accepted the quote and submitted your agreement, the work has to be scheduled; this again is often weeks, or months, ahead of it being carried out. It will help if you dig the trenches for them yourself – just not very much. Indeed, there are usually no discounts available for helping or making life easier for them, and your only motivations for doing so may be to control where the hole in your land occurs and to speed up the process a bit. Supplies for gas, water and electricity can all be brought in via the same trench, as long as it is deep enough to get the water at the bottom, then the gas and electricity above at a minimum separation distance, and still be deep enough for protection backfill over the top.

In addition to their charges for carrying out the connection work (which incidentally is quickly executed once they are on site), there are 'infrastructure' charges to be added on, which you must also pay for simply adding an extra home to the national grid. As these charges are added per home, in a development of several apartments, they can add up to very large sums. The fact that all the cables or pipes may be laid in one trench and all the meter boxes grouped in line together to make the job easier does not reflect in the infrastructure charge; that simply multiplies with the number of homes created. What is really needed here is some healthy competition to allow registered firms to undertake connections and provide the equipment.

I can recall a time when at least the build-in meter boxes were free, but now they must be bought, too. Named builders merchants and suppliers are listed as stockists for them, so do not expect to be able to pick them up from anywhere.

Positioning the supply and meters

Siting of the boxes is something you do have some control over, although there are restrictions, especially for gas meters. The gas

▸ Choose between wall-mounted and semi-concealed (ground-level) meter boxes.

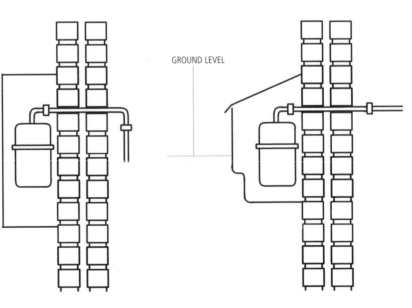

GROUND LEVEL

SURFACE MOUNTED METER BOX

SEMI-CONCEALED METER BOX

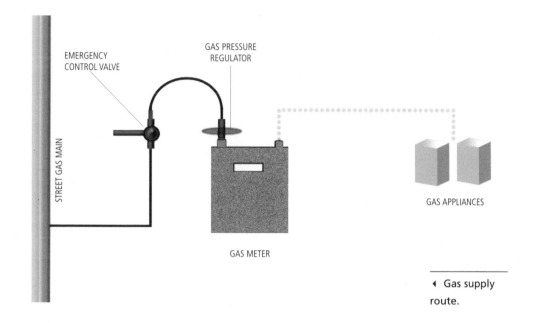

EMERGENCY
CONTROL VALVE

GAS PRESSURE
REGULATOR

STREET GAS MAIN

GAS APPLIANCES

GAS METER

◄ Gas supply
route.

and electricity companies that you subscribe to would like them to
be accessible for readings, but do not seem to be quite so
prescriptive as they have been in the past.

If you do have a foot or two of land in front of the building
that is inside your boundary (and not belonging to the highway
authority), you might be able to have ground-level meters
installed. These are known as semi-concealed meter boxes because
they do not actually sit flush with the ground. Instead, they are
low to it, with sloping lids that sit proud by about 300 mm. Semi-
concealed meter boxes are often made in brown-coloured plastic
and are therefore less visually intrusive than the traditional wall
boxes, which were built in at chest height and always white. The
latter are rarely acceptable on listed buildings. A note of caution
has to be made with regard to these semi-concealed boxes: the
passing feet of local vandals have easily damaged a few that have
been set into the ground alongside public footpaths. Having
broken the meters, they can easily turn the gas off to properties.
The whole subject of vandalism is a depressing one to consider,
but the fact is it happens and this type of installation can make it
happen easily. Some security combined with reasonable access is
needed. Aside from vandalism, the ground box on the back edge
of pavements could be hit by accident if a car mounts the path, so
it will need some protection against this, too.

In apartment conversion projects furnished with gas supply, dividing the supply into separate meters for each apartment is essential. Gas governors, pipes and meters take up a lot of space, and finding somewhere to locate them inside the building is often a struggle. Outside meter cupboards are ideal; however, if they simply are not possible and you have no choice but to locate the meters inside, the next step is to see if you can keep them out of the stairway and any fire escape routes of apartment buildings. The hallways and stairways of Victorian homes are often not that wide (particularly once you have finished dividing the building and fire-protecting the enclosing walls). Sticking a lot of equipment on them can reduce this width even more. In truth, this is no doubt where the existing supply equipment resides, and you might wonder why on earth you should try to move it.

Gas is a potential fire risk, and the advice is that you should not create fire risks on escape routes, especially when they happen to be the only escape route available. Windows more than 4.5 m above ground level do not count as fire exits. That being the case, gas meters are better inside the apartments themselves, but that means splitting up the supply to the building. Outside should always be your first choice, and indeed in new-build developments the meters are often located externally in purpose-made supply porches or cupboards.

If you simply cannot fit them out there, you may be faced with having to install them in the hallway to the stairs. This may be acceptable as the last option, when you can protect them within a fire-resisting enclosure. That means boxing it in using 50 mm by 50 mm timbers to form a framework, then covering the framework on both sides with fire-rated cladding. Fire-rated 12-mm plasterboard will do the job if you want to plaster finish and decorate it. Better still, cement fibreboard makes a far more robust material. It is also ideal for lining the cupboard doors to achieve at least 30 minutes' fire resistance. If the boarding is screwed to the framework and sealed around the edges with fire-rated silicone mastic, forming a neat box enclosure, it will do the job required.

This seems like the safe and sensible thing to do, but you may have to convince your gas supply inspector that it is. The last two projects I looked at where the carpenters had made a wonderful job of fire-protecting the gas equipment this way, the inspector made them remove it on the basis that, if there was a gas leak, nobody would know. This casing was not airtight, but it had not been supplied with any ventilation to the outside, and the inspector can insist that the enclosure is ventilated by non-combustible pipework. The purpose for this is to vent any gas leak inside the enclosure and prevent it going unnoticed and building up. This is the advice contained within the Gas, Safety and Use Regulations, and it makes more sense than simply removing the cupboard and leaving the gear on show and at risk of fouling your fire escape route.

I would also suggest you set the enclosure reasonably high on the wall if you can, out of reach of small children, but still accessible to adults. The doors should be secured anyway, and tenants can always be given a meter box key to open them. This together with a sign stating 'Fire door. Keep locked shut' should be enough to make sure that it is kept closed.

If you do have to vent the box with a pipe to external air, use the steel gas pipe that you can buy from plumbers' merchants and paint it, or use plastic waste pipe encased within fire-rated ducting. You may have to make this up with the boxing itself. It does not really matter where you vent the box to, as long as it is to the outside and not to the loft space or some other enclosed void. I tend to think a vent grille above the main entrance door (or near to it) is a good place to terminate it, as any gas leak will be noticed by people coming and going.

Electric coin meters

Pay-as-you-go metering for electricity is still common in tenanted property. The difficulty comes in mews apartments and maisonettes with siting the meters and their boxes because most electricity distributors will not bring the main up through a building above ground level. If the common entrance hall is on the first floor, perhaps above a shop or a ground-floor home, the meters will have to be located outside the building. From therein, the supply is your responsibility as it arises. Having pay-as-you go meters outside and remote from the apartments themselves is not ideal for tenants when the power has run out. They are best installed internally in communal meter cupboards.

Altering an existing gas supply

It is not unusual for a meter and its supply pipe to need moving or altering when homes are divided. The work cannot be done simply by a CORGI-registered fitter, but must also be carried out by your gas supplier. It is difficult to imagine how much more controlled this procedure could be and, to help guide you through it, the National Grid has produced a 15-page guidebook as a summary of the process. In a nutshell, gas pipes can no longer be installed underneath buildings and consequently it is not possible to build an extension over a gas supply pipe or re-route a supply pipe under the floor.

It was the case in years gone by that you could, as long as the pipe was sleeved and protected from encasement, but all that has changed now. Those of you unlucky enough to discover the gas supply in the ground beneath your intended annexe or apartment will have to pay for it to be re-routed around it. This seems to have taken priority over the supply being visible and at risk from accidental damage or vandalism, and it is not uncommon these days to see gas pipes running great distances around the external walls of homes. Gas, unlike water, does not freeze, and these pipes can also be clipped to the external surface of walls, unprotected from the elements. The gas company will usually expect you to pay for excessive supply pipework en route to your meter. Indeed, charges are currently based on how much pipework is needed.

Below-ground (buried) pipe up to your meter from the national grid is now made of plastic and colour-coded yellow for identification. The pipe can be detected by meters before any digging starts, but these are not always accurate, and nor are the pipes laid in straight lines – they can weave and wander all over the place, so dig cautiously. Previously steel pipe was used, but this is prone to corrosion and has become a problem now. If you have an existing supply in steel, you may be able to avoid the cost of it being replaced in today's pipe. Replacing the old steel pipework whenever they get the chance is in the gas companies' best interests, so let them know.

The meters, some 21 million of them in the United Kingdom, remain the property of the gas transporter, and they have limitations on where they can be sited. It might be easier to look at where you cannot install them, rather than where you can.

Where you cannot locate gas meters
1. Where it will be a danger to any persons
2. Where it is unreasonably remote from where the gas supply enters the building
3. Where it is inaccessible for inspection, index reading, emergency control valve operation, adjustment of the governor, servicing and replacing
4. Where it is in contact with concrete or a frequently wet floor
5. Where it is closer than 150 mm to an electricity meter
6. Where food is stored
7. Where it is closer than 300 mm to the flue pipe of any gas appliance
8. Where it will be subjected to extremes of temperature or close to a heat source, e.g. boiler rooms, south-facing conservatories
9. Where it might be liable to damage or cause an obstruction

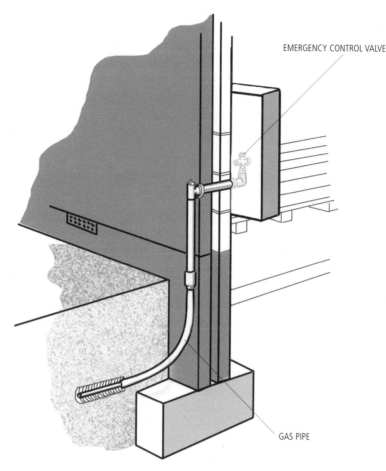

EMERGENCY CONTROL VALVE

◀ Internally, domestic gas meters cannot be located in certain positions.

GAS PIPE

10. Where it might be exposed to corrosive liquid or atmosphere, such as beneath a kitchen sink

11. Under stairs or in the common parts of apartment buildings that serve as the only means of escape route in a fire, unless the meter is enclosed in a 30-minute fire-rated cupboard

In reality, there are only so many places where you can stick your gas meters, and frankly you will be lucky if it is a perfect location. Compromises have to be made, and it is a case of finding the best location for your building.

Types of meter box
◆ Built-in cavity wall meter box
◆ Surface-mounted meter box
◆ Semi-concealed meter box

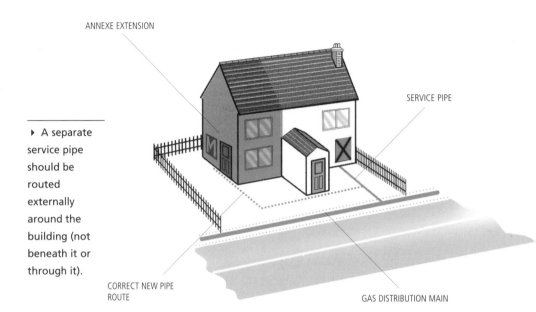

ANNEXE EXTENSION

SERVICE PIPE

▸ A separate service pipe should be routed externally around the building (not beneath it or through it).

CORRECT NEW PIPE ROUTE

GAS DISTRIBUTION MAIN

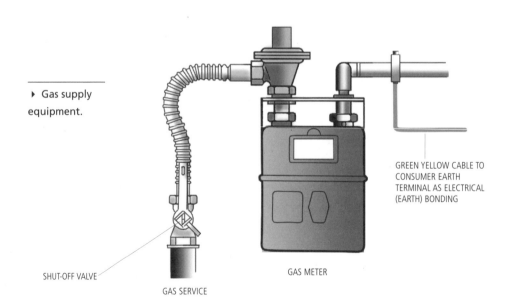

▸ Gas supply equipment.

GREEN YELLOW CABLE TO CONSUMER EARTH TERMINAL AS ELECTRICAL (EARTH) BONDING

SHUT-OFF VALVE

GAS SERVICE

GAS METER

Most builders install built-in meter boxes in new homes. The box is recessed into the outer wall, and only the door sits proud of the wall face. These were once provided free of charge, but now must be purchased as well as installed by your builder. This type of box is usually positioned at a height of between 500 mm and 1000 mm above the ground (to the bottom of the box).

Surface-mounted boxes are provided and fitted by the gas company as part of its connection work. They are located between 500 mm and 1500 mm of the ground; however, as they project out around 250 mm from the face of the wall, they have to be located where you are not going to bump into them. This means away from a narrow pathway or perhaps tucked into an internal corner out of the way.

Semi-concealed meter boxes, as discussed earlier, sit low to the ground with sloping lids. They usually extend from the ground by about 300 mm.

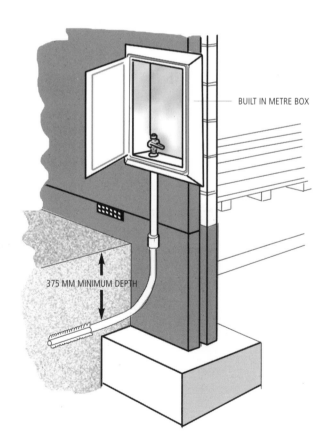

BUILT IN METRE BOX

375 MM MINIMUM DEPTH

◄ New gas supply should be buried at least 375 mm deep below ground.

EMERGENCY
CONTROL VALVE

▸ Semi-
concealed
ground
meter box.

375 MM MIN.
DEPTH (PRIVATE)

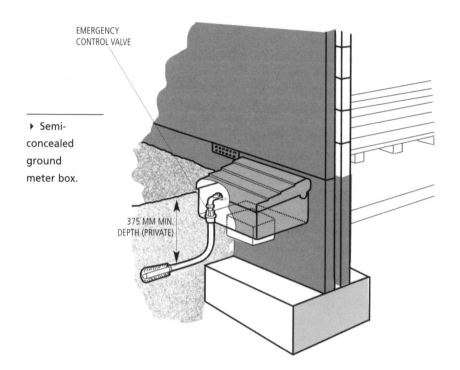

INSET METER
BOX

EMERGENCY
CONTROL VALVE

▸ Surface
mounted
meter box.

375 MM MIN.
DEPTH (PRIVATE)

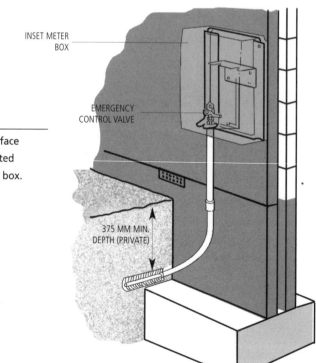

Although the gas transporter will install the supply up to the meter and the meter equipment, from here on in to your property the gas supply should be piped to where it is needed by a CORGI-registered engineer. The size of supply pipe will determine the flow of gas at the appliance, and consequently it is important not to undersize the supply pipe.

Water supply

Water is somewhat different to gas and electricity because you own and take responsibility for everything inside your boundary from the stopcock on the mains onwards. In other words, the buried supply pipe from there to your home is for you to install and maintain at your expense.

Your water authority will be able to draw a new supply to the building if it is needed for the increased use, but at a healthy charge. For those multi-storey buildings running sprinkler systems along with the domestic water demand, large-diameter rising mains may have to be tapped into the distributor main, and you can expect four-figure sums to appear on the invoice. The distributor mains are

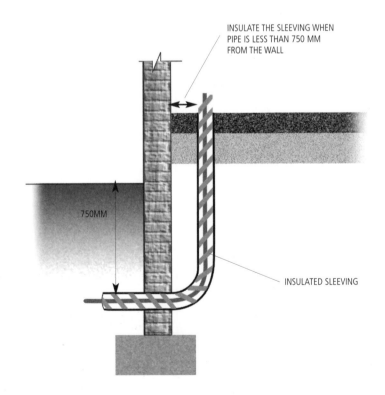

INSULATE THE SLEEVING WHEN PIPE IS LESS THAN 750 MM FROM THE WALL

750MM

INSULATED SLEEVING

◄ Incoming water supply pipes should be encased in sleeving (ducting) passing through solid concrete floors.

▸ Insulated
sleeving to
water pipes
terminating at
floor boarding
in suspended
timber ground
floors.

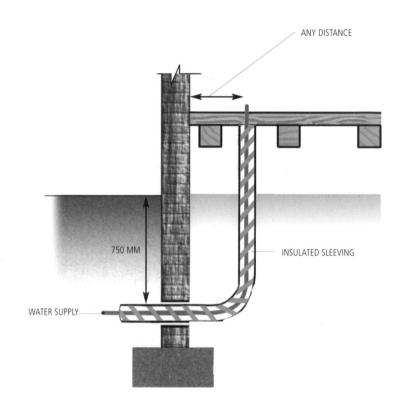

ANY DISTANCE

750 MM

INSULATED SLEEVING

WATER SUPPLY

invariably large-diameter cast-iron affairs, pitted with rust over the decades. These are tapped into, with stop valves in place to release the supply when all is ready. The supply to your homes will be in aqua blue alkathene material – a tough plastic pipe.

For a new home, whether it is an apartment or a maisonette, a separate independent water supply is as necessary as separate gas and electricity supplies. From the water mains the blue alkathene pipe is used to bring the water up to the property. For some time now, water to new dwellings has had to flow through a meter, and the meter has been installed by the water company at the boundary to your property. That means below ground in the path, where a small square steel lid can be prised open for you to peer down into to read a meter gauge that sits near the stopcock at a funny angle. They are not exactly user-friendly. That could change.

In 2006, for the first time I viewed a water meter attached to the outside wall of the home, alongside the gas and electric meters. The plastic meter box was heavily insulated with polystyrene to avoid the supply freezing, but, even so, the meter nestled inside it was easy to read. The only drawback was that the water company refused to use it instead of the hole-in-the-

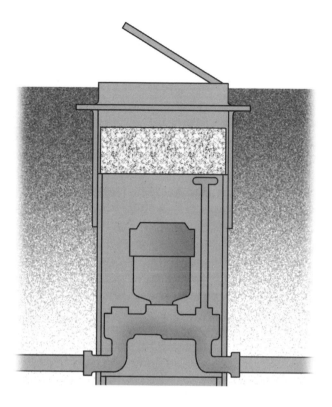

◄ Cross-section
through a
buried water
meter and stop-
cock on
incoming
supply.

pavement type, only as a 'consumer extra' to the hole in the
pavement – which sort of defeats the object.

With water supply, you can either provide separate supply pipes
into the building, one for each property, or bring in one supply pipe
to a multi-valve inside the building, which then splits off into
separate supplies. For buildings with a large number of apartments,
the valve and indeed the supply pipe can be monstrously sized and
difficult to house in the entrance of the building. The installation
that you end up with has much to do with the water company's
preferences and access for the supply to the building.

Gas boilers

Some 1.6 million new boilers are fitted every year now, each
packed with new technology and a host of tiny electronic and
mechanical parts – all prone to failure. The new generation of
boilers may be far more energy efficient in their use of fuel, but
not in the manufacture of their parts, which regularly need
replacing. The life expectancy of most is much shorter than that
of their predecessors, which could be expected to serve for 20 or
30 years without failing.

▸ Water-supply control and secondary backflow protection to each flat.

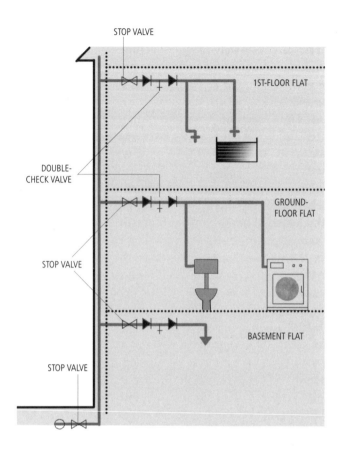

STOP VALVE

DOUBLE-CHECK VALVE

STOP VALVE

STOP VALVE

1ST-FLOOR FLAT

GROUND-FLOOR FLAT

BASEMENT FLAT

COLD-WATER CISTERN

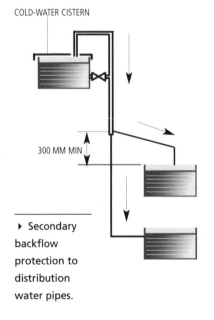

300 MM MIN

▸ Secondary backflow protection to distribution water pipes.

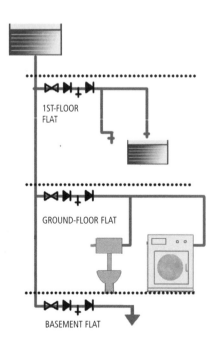

1ST-FLOOR FLAT

GROUND-FLOOR FLAT

BASEMENT FLAT

Technology comes at a price, and for boilers that price is robustness. They are relatively fragile machines in a hostile environment, and one of the first things to bring them down is the sludge in the water of an old central heating system. Simply removing the old boiler and sticking a new one onto the system is not an option. The system of pipes and radiators will be clogged by black water and sediment built up over years of use; while your old boiler may have been able to cope with it, the new one will not. It will soon be clogged and break down.

Installers of replacement boilers are obliged to flush the old system clean before fitting them, and that is not easy. The radiators will have a thick sludge in the bottom that can often only be removed by taking them off the wall, hauling them outside and flushing them through with a hosepipe until the water runs clear. Flushing a system is possible in situ, but it takes time and may not be all that successful. A power flush with a chemical additive to try to free up the sludge (which consists of blackened metal particles) is essential, but it can turn an old heating system into a sprinkler system, as the chemical is aggressive and can attack weak pipes and joints, creating leaks. This is a frightening prospect and not one that anybody will take responsibility for if it happens.

Cleaning the system cannot be avoided, but toning down the chemical additive to a weaker grade and supplementing the boiler

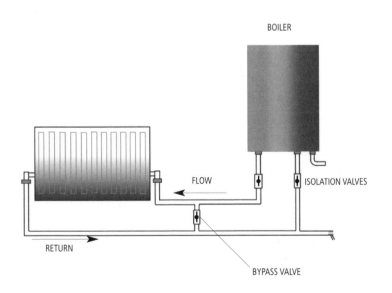

BOILER

FLOW

ISOLATION VALVES

RETURN

BYPASS VALVE

◄ Sealed heating systems with bypass are ideal for small divided homes.

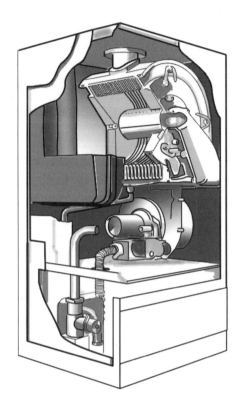

▶ Exploded view of combination boiler.

protection with a filter device can reduce the risks. These filters are fitted just ahead of the boiler on the return-flow pipework and incorporate an electro-magnetic filter that attracts the metallic black sludge as it flows through the water. The filter can be removed periodically for cleaning, and refitted.

Heating oil

In rural areas, often mains gas is not available. Instead heating oil is the most common form of fuel. If you are extending a rural home to provide an independent annexe, chances are you will need to upgrade your existing fuel tank or install another smaller one. Invariably old tanks are made from steel (painted green) and are smelly and inappropriately sited. They may even leak. Replacing a tank is well worth doing.

Most oil storage tanks do not exceed 3500 litres in capacity, and these are described as the 'Class 1' type. Today they are plastic and invariably double-skinned or bunded, to avoid risk of leakage.

Storing any amount of fuel, let alone a few thousand litres of it, introduces some safety requirements, and the first is the siting of the tank. It should not be too near the house or the boundary of your property. Too close to either will create the potential for fire spread. A distance of 1.8 m from the outside walls of your home and 760 mm from the boundary is considered the minimum. If you find it impossible to locate your new tank at such as a distance, it becomes necessary to enclose it with a fire-resistant structure. You may have seen some tanks hidden inside brick walls because, in truth, plastic oil tanks are equally as unsightly as the old metal ones. Many people choose to hide them inside a brick enclosure and grow plants against it. As long as you keep the wall and the foliage 600 mm away from the tank, it will not come to any harm. This also gives you the opportunity of tucking it away in a corner of your garden. The only consequence comes from having to run a 10-mm oil supply pipe underground to your boiler for a greater distance. Access for refilling the tank is obviously essential, but some of the tankers use long hoses that can reach quite some distance from the truck, perhaps as much as 20 m when necessary.

If you do not like the thought of an oil tank in your garden, screened or not, it is possible to install an underground storage tank. These can sometimes be installed closer to buildings and boundaries, but it is essential that they are not deeper than your foundations nor close enough to rob support from them when the hole is excavated. Buried oil tanks suffer the same problem as cesspools and septic tanks; in wet ground they can become buoyant and float to the surface. It is not a good idea to install them in wet clay soil, which can swell in winter and heave them upwards.

A concrete overcap will help to keep them in the ground when they are empty, but it cannot always guarantee it. All underground tanks are fitted with overfill protection to avoid spillage during the refilling process. Both the fire risk and the environmental hazard must be considered by the installer, and a risk assessment form is usually completed. When finding a suitable installer, look for somebody who is registered with OFTEC (Oil Firing Technical Association), which is the governing body in oil installations. Membership is not compulsory, but it does allow operatives to self-certify their work. Just be aware that the association qualifies its members for various tasks separately – oil storage tank installation, boiler installation, boiler commissioning – and hence they are specialists in particular tasks.

Hot water

For apartments and truly self-contained annexes, total control of hot water and heating is best achieved by installing a combi boiler. With these boilers, all of the ancillary plumbing – tanks, vessels, pumps and valves – is either cancelled out or miniaturised into the boiler itself, and hence they occupy the least amount of space. They are relatively cheap to buy, but not so cheap to maintain. They also come with a pretty short life expectancy. Even so, of the 1.6 million boilers installed every year in the United Kingdom, combis represent the majority.

Storing hot water

For an apartment or maisonette, you might like to consider storing hot water under pressure in a sealed system. Unvented cylinders will run a mixer shower with some pressure, something a combi boiler cannot do. These stores can be large enough to provide ample hot water for showers and other uses simultaneously. As unvented cylinders, they are sealed systems that deliver hot water at mains pressure and now account for a third of all hot water systems in new UK homes.

The smaller ones (50–100 litres) can be wall-mounted and might be small enough (about 500 mm in diameter and 700 mm high) for an annexe to have its own hot-water store, but really the market has been with the large floor-standing units of up to 500 litres. They can be heated by electricity or by a gas or oil-fired boiler. Once again, the electric option saves space, but economical they are not unless you can heat the store up at night on cheap-rate power. The temperature of the water stored inside them is perhaps as high as 80°C, so a lot of insulation is needed and the factory fitted lagging is not always enough. I have known cylinders to be fitted into the cupboards of bedrooms and the heat generated by them has made it impossible to sleep. You can buy insulation jackets to add over the top of any factory lagging, and remember that, within a metre of any hot-water store, the hot pipes should be insulated to prevent heat loss.

Find a location that is big enough and suitable enough for a large store that will serve both your home and the new divided annexe simultaneously. Roof spaces of maisonettes or annexes, as well as kitchens, are also not out of the question.

The problem comes when you have a small hot-water storage tank that is incapable of filling a bath in one go. Hence it becomes necessary to use a full cylinder of very hot water, cooled with plenty of cold to get the temperature you want. I used to have a small dual-coiled cylinder that was quick to reheat, but could only manage a third of a bath at a time. Frankly, when I take a bath, I like to get more than a third of myself wet.

Flues

For years, the combi boiler has been perfect for apartments and maisonettes, and almost the only solution. Combis are quite

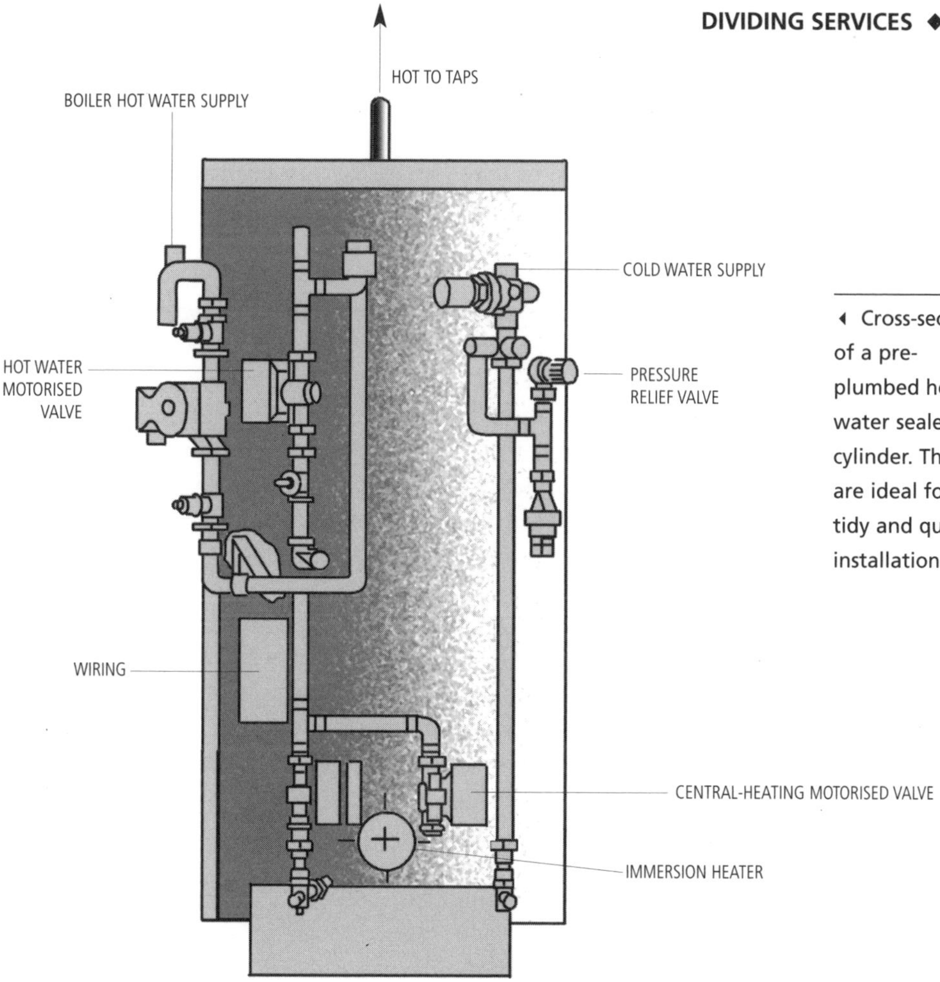

BOILER HOT WATER SUPPLY

HOT TO TAPS

COLD WATER SUPPLY

HOT WATER
MOTORISED
VALVE

PRESSURE
RELIEF VALVE

WIRING

CENTRAL-HEATING MOTORISED VALVE

IMMERSION HEATER

◂ Cross-section of a pre-plumbed hot-water sealed cylinder. These are ideal for tidy and quick installation.

versatile and can be fitted in different locations as long as the flue can be run out in a suitable place. As with many boilers, the fluing can be extended vertically or horizontally, or a mixture of both to find a suitable outlet position. Distances of 4–5 m (room width) for the flue length are not unusual, and so the boiler does not even have to be located on an outside wall.

The flue does have to have its outlet in fresh air, however, and in fact it is the flue terminal that often decides where the boiler will be sited. It has never been easy, finding the right spot to exhaust boiler flue gases. They cannot discharge beneath windows, under roofs, in corners or near extractor fan vents, among others things, but more often than not the real problem lies in the boundary. Extractors should not be located on walls within a metre of the boundary. In urban Britain, the side walls of our homes are often closer than this to the boundary and, as a result, flues can possibly cause a nuisance to neighbours. Indeed, they often do and, although gas boilers themselves can be installed by self-certificating CORGI engineers, even they are occasionally prone to 'relaxing' this requirement when there is no other place for the boiler to be installed.

The repercussions of nuisance flues often reach the local council as neighbour complaints, and it is becoming a bigger problem now that condensing boilers are mandatory. Condensing boilers have exhaust fumes that plume out rather like the contrail of an aircraft. The by-product of their high efficiency is a cloud of water vapour that is pumped by a fan out of the flue terminal to billow into the fresh air. Here it cools rapidly into water droplets and settles over anything nearby, whether that is the neighbour's car or patio furniture, or your own front door. Not surprisingly, this has led to most new-house builders installing condensing boilers on the front or rear walls of the house, but that can be just as annoying. On a crisp winter's morning I took a stroll along one of the new 'urban village' roads nearby. On this development all of the boilers had been installed in the kitchens alongside the front door, and hence all of the flue outlets were poking out of the walls alongside the front door. It was about 8 am and frosty, and all of the boilers were running, a fact that was obvious because the entire road frontage was shrouded in fog.

▸ Boiler flues often determine where boilers are positioned.

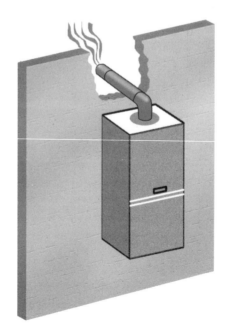

In mainland Europe, they have solved this problem by using vertical flues that rise like chimney stacks through the roof. There is no reason why we should not be doing the same in Britain. The boiler does not need to be in the kitchen. It can be in the loft if all the pipes are lagged. We need to start thinking about boiler flues in the same way we think of chimney flues – not many people would consider letting the smoke from the chimney pour out through the wall. I'm not suggesting that it is smoke – it is not – but it is a combustion by-product and it needs to disperse into a crossflow of air where it will not re-enter a building or become a nuisance to anyone. If you have to run it out through a side wall, it is still often possible to turn it vertically up the wall for couple of metres, then out. A couple of metres gives the plume a chance to disperse above people, but it does not look pretty having a flue pipe running up the outside wall of your home. All things considered, I would recommend finding a place where you can take the flue vertically out through the roof, chimney style, and terminate it with a weathering cowl.

Condensing boilers also have to be connected to the drains if the condensate is to be removed, and there is plenty of it. This means that they have to have a drain-off point where it can run into the above-ground plumbing or below-ground drainage system. The small (usually 28 mm in diameter) plastic pipe that carries the condensate away to the drains is connected to a water trap fitted inside the boiler that enables the pipe to be joined up to the foul drainage system without any of the foul air escaping into the home. In most new installations, the drain is plumbed into the waste pipe under a kitchen or utility sink, but it can equally connect to a rainwater pipe or a soil vent stack on the outside wall. In mainland Europe, nobody cares much about the condensate drain, and it is often left to run off onto the ground, but in the United Kingdom it should be connected up, even if it is only to a soakaway pit.

The condensate is not quite as pure as you might think. It contains some acid and there is some debate about whether it should be released to a soakaway or the surface-water drains of your home, or whether it should run straight to the foul drainage. Some manufacturers suggest it is no more acidic than rainfall, but I have never seen them prove this by drinking it. Indeed, some companies who make condensing boilers also make sumps and pump kits to go beneath boilers where no drainage exists, so that the water can be collected and removed to a more distant drain.

Some boiler manufacturers make small prefabricated soakaways with carbon fillings to collect the water and disperse it into the subsoil. As with all soakaways, they should be located away from the house. They have a cartridge chamber filled with carbon to neutralise the acid and release the condensate into the ground free of pollution. These miniature treatment tanks do not take up a lot of room and can be installed into a fairly small hole in the ground as an alternative to the sump and pump kits. A typical hole size of about 450 mm deep with a diameter of 150 mm will house one of these chambers, around which the hole is backfilled with gravel.

Both of these measures are solutions where no drainage exists around the boiler's location, but the usual arrangement is to run the plastic condensate drain pipe out from beneath the boiler and connect it up to the sink waste or above-ground drainage system. Plastic pipe must be used, not copper or steel, because of the acidic element.

We go to great lengths to take our waste water away in drain pipes, then replace it at great expense with fresh water. The condensate in this case is not so polluted that it can't be used for something. If you have a recycling system for toilet-flush or washing-machine water, then adding this to the system makes sense. If nothing else, it can top up the rainwater butt and be used in gardening. In the same way that a condensing tumble dryer collects the condensed water for emptying, the condensed water from a condensing boiler could be collected and used for plants. A water butt outside collecting the condensate would be ideal, but it should have an overflow to take the water away to drainage. Even if the water is slightly acidic, if you happen to have plants that enjoy acid conditions, such as rhododendrons and azaleas, this could be a benefit. Water from condensate is likely to be devoid of much in the way of nutrients, but a splash of liquid tomato food added to it and I'm sure you could water your plants through a drought.

More trouble with flues

Apart from the pluming nuisance with flues, you also need to deal with a detailed directive outlining how far away a flue terminal should be from just about any external bit of your home. In this case, it is aimed at getting the fumes away and dispersed into the atmosphere. In addition to all these dimensions, which apply to the building on which the boiler is fitted, it is also recommended that they should not face within 1 m of the boundary.

All of these limitations, added to the other gas safety liabilities that gas boilers bring, have driven many property developers dividing homes away from gas altogether. Instead, they have gone electric.

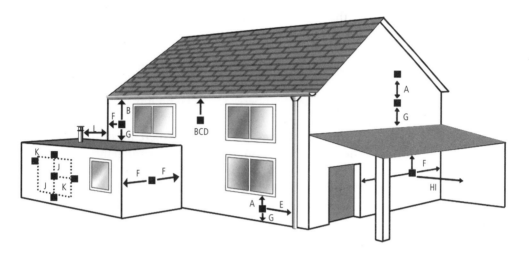

▲ Siting of boiler flues.

Siting of boiler flues

	REQUIRED DISTANCE OF FLUE TERMINAL FROM EXTERNAL PARTS OF BUILDING	
A	Directly below an opening, above an opening or horizontal to an opening such as a window, air brick or vent	300 mm
B	Below gutters, soil pipes or drain pipes	75 mm
C	Below eaves	200 mm
D	Below balconies	200 mm
E	From vertical drain pipes and soil pipes	25 mm
F	From internal or external corners	300 mm
G	Above ground, roof or balcony	300 mm
H	From a surface facing a terminal	600 mm
I	From a terminal facing a terminal	1200 mm
J	Vertical from a terminal on the same wall	1500 mm
K	Horizontal from a terminal on the same wall	300 mm
L	Distance from adjacent for vertical flue	500 mm

Electric heating

Billed as the cleanest and most convenient of fuels, electricity for heating is making a bit of a comeback. Electricity is technically 100 per cent efficient in use because no heat is lost out of the flue in burning it – because there is not a flue. This fact would serve electric heating well in terms of energy efficiency and the reduction of carbon dioxide emissions if we could produce electricity without burning gas or coal. In Britain, most of our electricity is produced from burning these fossil fuels, and consequently electric heating is not really a green choice. Choosing electricity from green providers using wind farms and the like, however, could change all that. In the future, electric heating and hot-water systems may be the only energy-efficient choice.

The big advantage of electric heating lies in the installation. It is trouble-free to install, with no fuel storage or flue problems to overcome. The problem comes with the running cost. Electricity is currently the most expensive way of heating both space and water. Electric radiator manufacturers have tried to tackle this problem with storage radiators that burn cheaper off-peak electricity (at night), gradually building up a thermal store within. To put it simply, they heat up built-in bricks. During the day, those brick stores release the heat into the room, whether you wanted it or not. With these radiators, you have to guess how much heat you want or whether you want any at all the next day before you set them to charge overnight. Realising the limitations of storage heaters, the manufacturers have tried to overcome this problem with convection-radiator functions incorporated with the storage type, as well as greater controls. This way, if you need to run your electricity bill through the roof unexpectedly on a cold day, you can.

The running costs are down to the tenant and, if they cannot afford them, they go cold. Where I live, in the southeast, the low-cost tariff occurs for only a short period during the night and, to avoid anyone taking advantage, the supplier frequently changes the times when it is supplied. In the dead of night, they will simply spike up the cost to standard rate to catch out people with programmable washing machines. It is not like that everywhere. In parts of Scotland, for example, blessed with their own hydro-electricity and longer colder periods, low-cost electricity is often available for much of the morning as well as the night.

If you are going to use any form of electric heating, it is absolutely imperative to make sure that you can take advantage of low-cost electricity and that you have a highly insulated, draught-free environment able to hold on to a comfortable level of background heat. The newest radiators, which are slightly more intelligent, can produce heat from different sources – a primary radiant element on the front face of the radiator panel which provides instant warmth, and a storage part that can maintain some background heat using night-time lower cost electricity. There are limits to the technology in this field. To try to overcome the problems with convection storage units, however, better controls have been added to the new models. These monitor the room temperature and release heat when it is needed. In other words, they raise the room temperature to the preset temperature

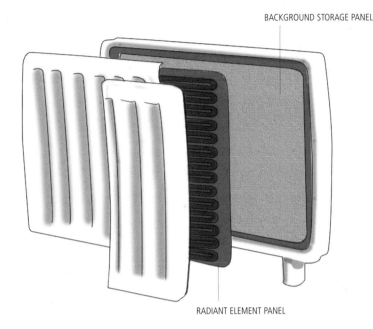

BACKGROUND STORAGE PANEL

RADIANT ELEMENT PANEL

◀ Some electric radiators have storage and instant-heat options.

requested by the occupier. From the occupier's point of view, it should mean that the heat is released in a more controlled way, but, without a programmable room thermostat controlling different temperature settings throughout the day, I cannot see it being any more economical. If you must have electric heating, however, there is another choice.

Electric boilers

Not surprisingly, all of the restrictions and problems associated with gas- and oil-fired boilers can cause you to wonder if there is no easier alternative. Well, there is. Electric radiators may have been the only choice for half a century, but now we have electric boilers, too. They can heat water and pump it around a conventional wet radiator system just the same as a gas- or oil-fired boiler does. The systems are sealed and therefore pressurised the same as any other unvented system, but with some attractive benefits for the installer. First, there are no by-products of combustion and hence no flues to worry about. Secondly, there are no condensate drains required. Thirdly, electric boilers are a fraction of the size of most gas- and oil-fired ones. They heat the water very quickly from a cold start, too, and require less maintenance.

They have one problem, and it is a big one if you are the occupier – they cost a fortune to run. Electricity may be clean to burn and trouble-free to maintain, but, compared to gas and oil, it is an expensive way to heat a building. If you do choose an electric boiler, I would strongly recommend that you ensure the divided home is very well insulated and able to retain heat effectively. These boilers are very quick to heat up a small space such as an apartment or an annexe. If the space is well insulated to the latest standards, that heat should stay put for hours after the boiler has switched off.

Electric boilers can be simply installed by wiring them in to a 32-amp circuit, and having no flue means that they can be installed in internal cupboards and the like. An RCD is always fitted to the electricity supply with these appliances, and it is important that the electrician installs the correct RCD for the boiler rating. Obviously, the higher the rated output, the higher the circuit current.

All in all a plumber's dream, the electric boiler can be installed in a fraction of the time it takes to install a gas or oil boiler, and without any of the headaches associated with fuel supply and flues. Not only that, but they are tiny and perfectly scaled for

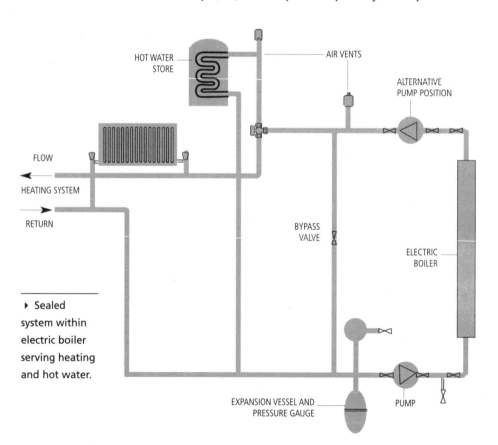

HOT WATER STORE

AIR VENTS

ALTERNATIVE PUMP POSITION

FLOW

HEATING SYSTEM

RETURN

BYPASS VALVE

ELECTRIC BOILER

▶ Sealed system within electric boiler serving heating and hot water.

EXPANSION VESSEL AND PRESSURE GAUGE

PUMP

small homes as well. Just heed my warning: if you will at some point have to run them during standard rate times, the kilowatts swallowed will spin your meter like a whirling dervish. In a converted apartment with poor insulation, they could prove to be too expensive for many occupiers to use, and once again they should only be installed in the most highly insulated buildings.

Boiler outputs can vary from 2 kilowatts up to 12 kilowatts or more, although you should aim for the smallest you need to heat the space. I would not use an electric boiler to heat a house, but, if you wanted to, you could link them to increase output. For example, you might use two 11-kW models side by side to achieve 22 kW of heat output for a house and annexe. Thermal calculations that take account of room volume and insulation values are the only way to accurately determine the size you need, but 9 kW should be more than enough for a new apartment. Typically, electric boilers are very small cylindrical appliances that look nothing like conventional boilers. A 2-kW model might contain only a litre of water and weigh around 7 kg. At only half a metre tall, it will fit in to the corner of a cupboard nicely. For a small apartment, a 6-kW model might be more suitable; with only twice the water content, it is not that much taller. They all tend to be modelled on the same diameter.

To be honest, the boiler is not the problem with small heating systems. It is the other equipment. Undoubtedly, a sealed system that needs no storage tanks or cylinders is ideal, if not essential, but these systems do need some equipment – notably the expansion relief vessel. This does not look any different to the expansion relief vessel associated with an unvented hot-water cylinder; being a little bulky, with associated pipework, valves and gauges attached, it takes up more space than the electric boiler itself.

Designed to work like an ordinary central heating, the water is run over an insulated copper or stainless-steel heat exchanger to raise its temperature as required. That could be to anything between 35° and 75°C, so they are quite versatile. The built-in electronics monitor the system and report on any defects, in the same manner as self-diagnostics do in cars these days. All the usual safety cut-outs exist, but one thing they are especially adaptable to is solar panels. Solar panels that preheat the water for free can be easily connected to most electric boilers, and that means that they do not have to burn so much electricity to raise the water temperature to the desired level. You might also decide to use underfloor heating with them, to free up wall space and ditch radiators altogether. As long as you include room thermostats to regulate room temperature and automatically shut the boiler down when no more heat is needed, it will comply with the Building Regulations and the referenced Domestic Heating Guide. The programmer may already be built in to set the on–off times, but if it is not a programmable room thermostat is the answer. I have had one of these for some years now, and they are wonderful. Not only can you set the times of day when you want the heating on, but you can also set the room temperature during that period and for each and every period, seven days a week.

From a maintenance point of view, gas and oil condensing boilers are a liability, but electric boilers are a different story. They give every indication of being cheaper to maintain, with far less serviceable parts. In terms of fuel efficiency, they hardly waste any at all, but that does not mean that they are cheap to run. The electric input is large all the same, and electricity is cheap only at set off-peak times and when you produce your own.

Electric unvented cylinders as thermal stores can also be used to run wet radiator systems on demand, but at least these large insulated cylinders can be wired to heat up automatically on the low tariff. Your electricity supplier will advise you, but automatic switching for appliances that you want to run this way is available. It at least means that the hot water can be heated as cheaply as possible and stored for use later in the day. If you need to boost it on demand, an override switch will do the job.

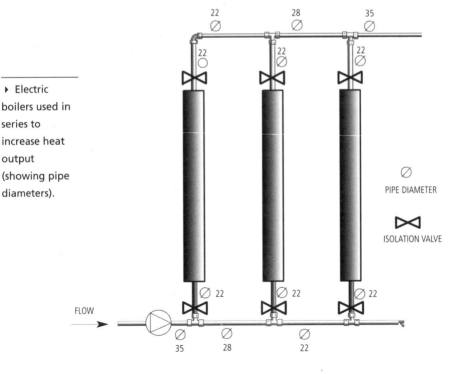

▸ Electric boilers used in series to increase heat output (showing pipe diameters).

Getting into hot water
Traditionally, boilers have been made to heat our water to about
60°C, a temperature that is more than hot enough to scald the
flesh off our bodies and cause painful burns. In 2006, a private
member's bill was tabled by an MP in the House of Commons
that called for thermostatic taps to be fitted in all bathrooms. It
drew a great deal of response from the media and public, much
of it criticising the 'nanny state' for trying to control every aspect
of our lives, including the temperature at which we choose to
wash ourselves.

In annexes for elderly parents, and indeed in homes with young
children, thermostatic devices are invaluable. Not surprisingly,
these are the people more at risk of scalding than anybody else.
Thermostatic taps, however, are not always reliable. Paying for a
quality make will help, but if you would rather not rely on the
taps to mix the hot and cold effectively, you might want to
consider a mixing valve ahead of them.
This is the method favoured in healthcare
premises, as it tends to be more reliable.
Thermostatic mixing valves incorporate a
temperature-sensitive element that controls
the water supply inlets, and the better
models will automatically shut off the
hot-water flow if the cold-water flow
fails for any reason.

Fitting devices that regulate the
temperature of bath water through built-
in thermostatic controls is a better option
in my mind than letting 60°C water rush
over your hands, but really it should be
left up to individuals as to where and
whether they are installed. When it comes
to showers, consumers have come to
value thermostatic devices. Nobody
wants to be standing naked in cascading
water when the temperature suddenly
shoots up to this mark, and most of these
devices are factory set at a limit of 43°C,
but remain adjustable.

Still, if we are trying to reduce the
temperature of our hot water with
expensive thermostatic devices, why are
we heating it up so much (at even more
expense) in the first place? Most boilers

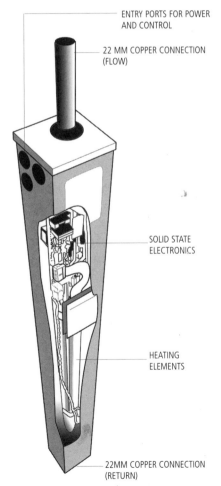

▾ Inside an
electric boiler.

ENTRY PORTS FOR POWER
AND CONTROL

22 MM COPPER CONNECTION
(FLOW)

SOLID STATE
ELECTRONICS

HEATING
ELEMENTS

22MM COPPER CONNECTION
(RETURN)

have been designed to run at 60°C. If you habitually set the thermostat on these boilers to run at 45°C instead, they soon start to rust away. Condensing boilers have had to be specifically designed to run at lower a temperature without suffering damage, something a non-condensing boiler just cannot do. Going back to the why question, as in why boilers have in the past aimed for the 60°C mark, you arrive at an ancient British Standard that involves the temperature at which mutton fat will melt. Very hot water is essential for cleaning crockery and kitchen utensils, but the truth is we need varying performance from our hot water throughout our homes, and not just temperature-wise. Pressure or flow rate varies from appliance to appliance as well. We need a carefully balanced flow rate in our mixer showers, but also a nice fast one to enjoy the showering experience. If you had the same pressurised delivery of water through the cloakroom taps into a small wash basin, you would be drenched the moment you turned on the taps to rinse your hands. Our demands for water pressure are just as variable as our demands for temperature.

It does not stop there either. In hard-water areas, limescale not only damages our washing machines and dishwashers, but also forces us to use more soap. What we really want is soft water that suds up easily and makes cleaning far less trouble, but it is essential to keep softened water away from the central heating system. The salts used in softening water react badly with the mixed metals in a heating system and cause corrosion and leaks. Most heating systems have steel radiators, copper pipes, brass valves and solder joints. Add water that is salt-laden to soften it and you have a recipe for emergency plumbing.

Controlling water

There are other devices apart from thermostatic devices that you can fit to regulate your water, in particular its pressure. You might think that simply adding ball service valves that can be turned slightly to restrict the flow will do the job, and you would be right – except for the fact that they tend to whistle continuously in the half-closed position.

Service valves are designed to be either off or on through a quarter turn with a screwdriver, and not halfway in between. To restrict the flow quietly, an in-line Bernoulli valve can be installed that looks much the same as a service valve, but uses a different method to reduce the water pressure (a series of tiny holes). Each will have a cap with a pre-printed flow rate on the top to enable you to select the right one for the each appliance and get the flow capped to the pressure you need. They are inexpensive to buy, but in hard-water areas they may become blocked periodically with limescale, and therefore need removing and cleaning as shower sprayheads do. You could fit the in-line valve between a service valve and the appliance it is serving if you have the space. This will allow you to isolate the water supply and remove the flow limiter for cleaning much more easily.

From a maintenance point of view, flow regulators do need to be removed before flushing out the system. Some are designed to allow you to close the ball valve (stopping the water flow), remove the colour-coded cap and unscrew the port cover. You can then use a pair of thin-nosed pliers to pluck out the regulator and reassemble the valve without the regulator inside. The system can then be flushed through. If the valve needs cleaning in white vinegar or something else to remove limescale, this can be done at the same time.

Just as the flow of electricity and gas varies to our homes with demand, so does the flow of water. The pressure of the incoming supply is perhaps the most variable of all the services, and by law water supply companies have to guarantee only a low pressure (about 1.5 bar), which is much less than most of us would like. In reality, pressures of 4 or 5 bar are typical, but this can peak in the dead of night when the demand drops, to as much as 10 bar. Ten bar of static water pressure will not trouble most of the taps on your system, but many showers cannot deal with it and will often blow a leak if not actually burst off the wall in the middle of the night. If you have ever woken to find your mixer shower leaking furiously but mysteriously, then this is probably why. As a result, shower manufacturers usually advise their customers to have flow limiters installed, preventing a build-up of static pressure.

Getting the flow rate right in showers is always difficult. Mixer showers have to be balanced correctly, and quite often the pressure differences between cold water and hot water arriving in the valve are extreme. Consequently, the shower struggles and

SUITABLE FLOW RATES FOR WATER CONTROL VALVES	
Appliance	Flow rate
WC cistern	4 L/min
Cloakroom hand basin	6 L/min
Large hand basin	8 L/min
Kitchen sink	10 L/min
Shower	12 L/min
Bath	18 L/min

fails to deliver water at the correct temperature and, if things get really bad, the mixer allows cold water to backflow down the hot-water supply and the boiler shuts down. Pressure can vary from 1 to 10 bar on the cold-water supply side.

As an alternative to the water control valves, there are some valves that can be fitted to the shower hose or riser pipe itself. They do the same job of limiting the flow rate, but this time between the shower valve and the sprayhead hose. They are easier to install in this position, but it is far better to install such a device ahead of the valve, in the supply pipe.

Controlling heating

As part of the energy-efficiency measures, heating controls are important to get right. They always have been the subject of much controversy and opinion. I can remember my neighbour swearing that it was far more efficient to run his heating 24/7 than have it come on and off with the programmer, and this was in the 1970s when our homes had just been installed with central heating for the very first time. We did not have much insulation then, and so by keeping the heating ticking over at a low level you did not let the house drop below its core temperature and need raising by a huge amount. I have always used a programmer to its maximum potential and I cannot bring myself to heat the house all day while it is empty. Underfloor heating systems are masters at maintaining a constant climate. The entire floor acts as a radiator panel and, as it is much bigger than the metal ones we hang on the walls, it can be heated to a lower temperature to achieve the same comfort level. Still, for some people, if you cannot touch a radiator and feel the heat, or stand in front of a fire and warm your hands, then the place is not heated at all. Regardless of whether or not they feel comfortable, they need to feel the heat source; with underfloor heating you cannot, unless you walk around in your socks.

Whatever your choice of heating, you must have controls to regulate it, and those controls must include a boiler interlock function. Boiler interlock means the boiler shuts off automatically when no heat is required, and does not keep on running hot water around pointlessly. The radiator valves that control the flow into individual radiators are fine, but they are mechanical devices and will not shut the boiler off electronically. If all of the thermostatic radiator valves (TRVs) on your system decide that the radiators have reached the preset temperature on the valve, the hot water is still circulated around the system; it simply does not flow through the radiators. The pipes will allow it to bypass the radiators and loop around and around, endlessly causing the boiler to fire up and heat the circulating water. This, therefore, is not boiler interlock.

In addition to the thermostatic radiator valves, you should fit a thermostatic room thermostat. Room thermostats send an electronic signal to the boiler once the required room temperature is reached, and this signal shuts the boiler down. Whatever the TRVs are saying, the room thermostat is the oracle – it decides when the home is warm enough. Traditionally, the room thermostat is placed in the hallway, but it could just as easily live in the lounge. Most heating engineers advise that you do not fit a TRV to the radiator in the same room as the room thermostat – an ordinary lockshield radiator valve will suffice. Even if your apartment is small, a room thermostat should control the boiler to regulate the heating. They have come a long way from those manual clocks on the wall that you wound around. Today's room thermostats are digital and may allow you to set the time with the temperature, and thus divide your day (and night) into separate temperature zones.

Well-insulated homes can be heated in half an hour, as long as they are not left to drop below their core temperature. In the same way that our bodies have problems recovering once our core temperature is lost, so do our homes. It takes them much longer to reheat and become comfortable again, which is why it is best to set your thermostats to prevent this happening. It may seem like madness to be out all day and heating your unoccupied home, but if you shut down the system completely every day the home's core temperature can drop very low. It will take a long time and a lot of expensive energy to bring it back up again, so leaving it to tick along while you are out makes sense as long as it provides just a gentle background heat. For most people, a temperature of perhaps 16°C or 17°C is fine at night or when you are absent because the boiler will not have to work too hard to raise it up to comfort levels in the morning or when you return. If it was left to drop down towards 10°C, you would have a lot of money to spend getting it back to the low twenties come start-up time. Insulation plays a great role in this scenario of course, and a small and well-insulated home should be very easy to keep at a suitable background temperature.

If you are away for several days in winter, you can afford to leave a lower setting of perhaps 7°C or 8°C, which will keep the boiler off except in cases of extreme cold where the system becomes at risk of damage. I have a small summerhouse in my garden that is insulated, and the temperature in winter never drops below 7°C inside it, so using this temperature setting is not a problem for modern homes. The boiler will remain mostly redundant at this time.

Electrical installations

The list of competent persons able to carry out electrical work under part P of the Building Regulations continues to grow as more trade bodies have schemes approved for their members. The main recognised bodies are the NICEIC (National Inspection Council for Electrical Installation Contracting) and the ECA (Electrical Contractors Association), but there are others. In employing them, you will receive a certificate of testing and compliance with the relevant standards of safety and quality for any work that they carry out. This is essential when it is 'notifiable work' under the Building Regulations. Notifiable work could mean adding extra power sockets or light points, and only a suitably qualified person (ie registered with the NICEIC or the ECA) will be able to self-certify the work and avoid a building control service application.

Rewired circuits

The job of rewiring a complete circuit should be carried out by a registered electrician who can cover his or her work as a self-certified 'competent person' and issue a Part P certificate of compliance for it. This certificate is meant for work subject to Part P of the Building Regulations that has been designed, constructed, inspected and tested in accordance with BS: 7671. If one person is responsible for all four of these, he or she has the honour of signing in that capacity. If separate individuals are responsible for each, the name, address and signature afforded to

---

ELECTRICITY FACTS

◆ Most cables run hot, at a temperature of about 79°C.

◆ Supply companies are allowed to vary the voltage up and down within limits. What used to be 240 volts variable by plus or minus 6 per cent is now 230 volts plus 10 per cent or minus 6 per cent.

◆ A typical supply during the day is about 243 volts or more; this might drop to 238 volts at evening peak times.

◆ Leaking current always finds its way back to the source, attempting to complete the circuit, whether through the ground, metal pipes or you.

◆ Without a circuit breaker tripping, you may never know when an earth connection has come loose. Live wires fizz when they come adrift or cease to work; earth wires do not.

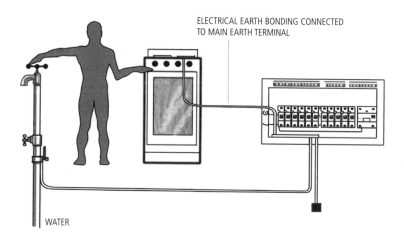

ELECTRICAL EARTH BONDING CONNECTED
TO MAIN EARTH TERMINAL

WATER

◄ Main earth
bonding in
electrical
installations to
prevent shock

each respectively is included on the certificate. It does not have to
be a complete rewire of the entire home to attract one of these.
Even minor alterations or additions to existing circuits in kitchens
and bathrooms are covered, too. Each circuit should be afforded a
schedule of inspection and testing. Remember to split lighting
circuits even if it is possible to connect them together; it pays
when one circuit is tripped out to have some light somewhere.

Alterations and checks

Although adding a plug point may seem like a minor task, there
are still five basic tests that are considered essential to doing so
correctly.

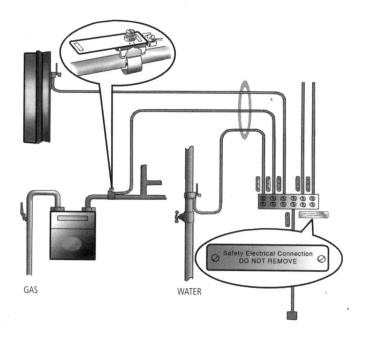

GAS   WATER

Safety Electrical Connection
DO NOT REMOVE

◄ Electrical
earth bonding
should be fitted
with warning
label tags.

▸ TN-S system.

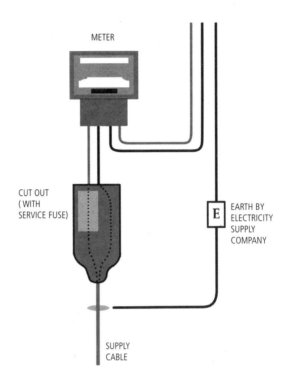

METER

CUT OUT
(WITH
SERVICE FUSE)

E EARTH BY
ELECTRICITY
SUPPLY
COMPANY

SUPPLY
CABLE

▸ TN-C-S (PME)
system.

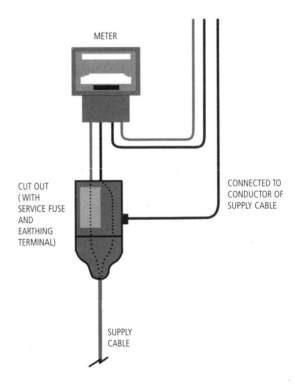

METER

CUT OUT
(WITH
SERVICE FUSE
AND
EARTHING
TERMINAL)

CONNECTED TO
CONDUCTOR OF
SUPPLY CABLE

SUPPLY
CABLE

They are:

1. Check that the earth contact of the socket outlet is properly connected to the main earthing terminal.
2. Measure the earth fault loop impedance and check that the maximum permitted disconnection time is not exceeded.
3. Measure the extended circuit's insulation resistance and check that it complies with BS 7671 requirements.
4. Check that the polarity of the socket-outlet is correct.
5. Check that the RCD (if there is one) works to still protect the circuit.

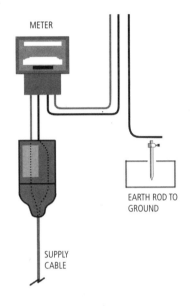

▲ T-T system.

Once installed and certified, all that remains is to check it annually to ensure it all is working correctly. For landlords, fire alarm systems, safety lighting and electrocution risks are at the heart of these periodic inspections.

You will need to commission a qualified and registered electrician who is able to issue a Periodic Inspection Report with reference to BS: 7671 (IEE Wiring Regulations). It has been specifically designed for checking existing installations only and not for carrying out new work. The purpose of the report should be stated on it, which could be to ascertain compliance with the current wiring regulations or perhaps simply to report on the safety condition of the cabling and equipment. Make sure that you and your electrician agree about what the purpose of the report is, and check that this is stated on the forms. The extent and any limitations of the report should also be clearly stated, although these should not appear in the form of a surprise – your contractor should have made you aware beforehand.

Reports are usually formed in sections and include the test results on the circuits, earthing arrangements and circuit breakers.

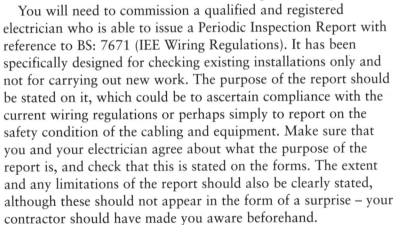

FOUR RATINGS FOR PRIORITISING ACTION	
1.	Requires urgent attention
2.	Requires improvement
3.	Requires further investigation
4.	Does not comply with IEE Wiring Regulations (current edition), but this does not mean that the installation is unsafe for use

Observations and recommendations are detailed and awarded ratings of priority for action (see table below).

Supply Earthing

There are three ways in which your new earthing conductor may be connected.

1. *TN-S system*

The electricity supply company provides the earth connection using the metal sheathing of the supply cable.

2 *TN-C-S system (aka PME, or protective multiple earthing)*

The electricity supply company provides the earthing connection using the neutral conductor of the supply cable. This is the norm for new connections, being the safest method.

3. *TT*

In this case, no suitable earth is available from the supply and you provide your own earth electrode (copper rod) anchored to the ground. Only 1 per cent of connections has to be made this way.

Above-ground drainage

Above-ground drainage systems have never been easier to install. Plastic drainage manufacturers provide an almost unimaginable catalogue of parts, to overcome all sorts of situations. It is simply a question of joining the pieces together correctly. The manufacturers have even made that task easier with the advent of push-fit plumbing to complement the traditional solvent-weld (glued joint) and compression (screwed joint) fittings. All that is required is a doable layout and a basic understanding of the things that you cannot do.

Five basic rules of above-ground drainage

1. Pipes have to be installed to falls, or gradients if you prefer, that allow the water to drain away effectively.
2. Appliances have to be fitted with water-seal traps that prevent that any foul drain smell from leaking into your home.
3. Air has to ventilate the system sufficiently to make sure those traps remain intact when the system is in use.
4. Measures have to be taken to ensure the pipework does not become blocked and uncleanable.
5. Pipes have to be properly sized for the job and their length, and properly supported by clips and fixings to keep them in place.

Equip yourself with a manufacturer's catalogue and make full use of the fittings to overcome problems with your layout. For example, you might face one of the problems below.

▲ Push-fit plumbing with greased seals.

Too many pipes?

Cutting down on the amount of pipework is always a good idea, so take the time to see how you can install a combined waste pipe that serves more than one appliance. Baths, basins and showers are prime examples and can all be joined into one pipe where they serve the same apartment and if the pipe is 40 mm or 50 mm in diameter, and no more than about 4 m long. As the basin drops down on top of the combined run that serves a bath or shower, it needs a swept connection that directs the flow the right way, and usually an anti-siphon trap is needed to prevent the trap being pulled out. I tried mine without one and it regularly pulled the trap on the shower waste outlet, causing much gurgling and some leakage of drain smells out of the shower. Once I replaced it with an anti-siphon trap with its built-in air miniature admittance valve, the problem was solved.

Cannot connect into the soil vent pipe?

Small waste pipes cannot connect into a vertical stack (SVP) directly opposite a larger pipe, such as a WC branch pipe, because soil water flowing into the vertical stack from the larger pipe is likely to block and 'crossflow' into the smaller pipe. The smaller pipe should connect at least 200 mm below or above the WC branch connection to avoid this occurring.

If a new bathroom has some waste pipes that need to be connected to an existing vertical soil stack, you may have problems joining them all in above the floor level. If the bathroom is upstairs and the soil stack is outside, the problem is not difficult to overcome. The lowest waste pipes serving the shower or bath can be dropped outside to join in at least 200 mm below the WC branch connection. The problems begin when the vertical stack is internal, as many are. You cannot break through the floor to make the connection at a lower level, although some people do if it can run between the floor joists. The joists cannot be cut to accommodate such large pipes.

Where this cannot be avoided because of floor levels and shower and bath waste pipes running above them, a collar boss may be

▶ Soil vent
stack with
branches and
traps fitted.

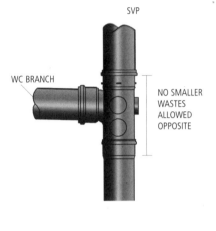

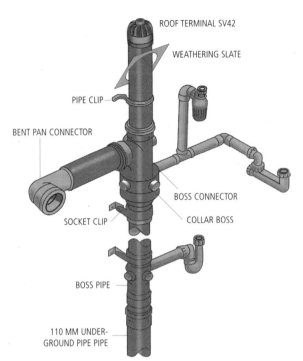

used directly under the WC branch – inside the 200-mm zone. This is possible if the collar boss fitting has an annular construction that allows the smaller waste pipes to flow outside the centre ring carrying the waste water from above. The pipes usually come with a selection of connection points that can be used if you need to run more than one shower or bath waste into them.

These pipes do not always look pretty in their battleship grey and, seen for the first time, some of these fittings can appear a bit Heath Robinson – particularly the flexi-pipe WC couplings. Correctly fitted, however, they are legal and they do work to overcome problems, so take advantage. The illustration on page 145 (bottom right) shows a typical collar boss in position.

Having planned your layouts for dividing homes, and the services, you are halfway there. Whether it is a simple annexe, a block of apartments or a luxury maisonette, trouble-free home-dividing lies ahead when you have a detailed

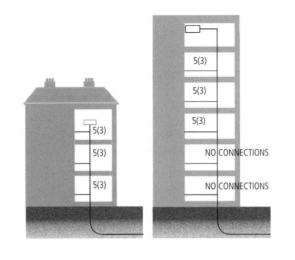

◂ A three-storey building can have up to five groups of appliances on each floor, all connecting to one SVP (soil vent pipe).

5(3)
5(3)
5(3)
5(3)
5(3)

5(3)
5(3)
5(3)
NO CONNECTIONS
NO CONNECTIONS

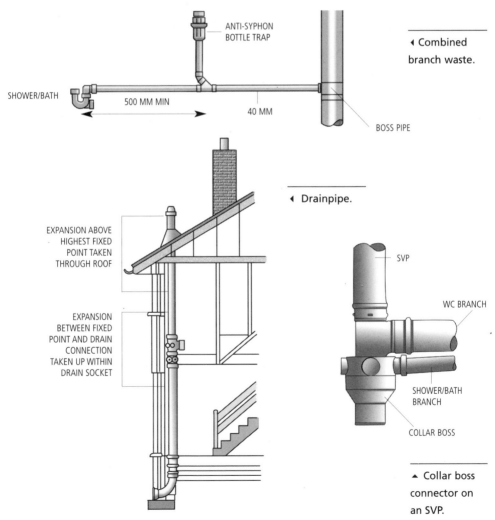

ANTI-SYPHON BOTTLE TRAP

◂ Combined branch waste.

SHOWER/BATH

500 MM MIN

40 MM

BOSS PIPE

◂ Drainpipe.

EXPANSION ABOVE HIGHEST FIXED POINT TAKEN THROUGH ROOF

EXPANSION BETWEEN FIXED POINT AND DRAIN CONNECTION TAKEN UP WITHIN DRAIN SOCKET

SVP

WC BRANCH

SHOWER/BATH BRANCH

COLLAR BOSS

▴ Collar boss connector on an SVP.

CHAPTER 5

Until recently, the only annexes I saw being built were for elderly parents and, in all honesty, I did not see them very often. Now all that has changed. Adding an annexe to the home is becoming much more common, and not just for the grandparents. Children who reach adulthood only to discover they have as much chance of going to the moon as they have of buying a starter home are needing annexes, too. In other countries, such as Italy, and within other cultures where generations of the same family have some tradition of living under the same roof, the idea of creating independence with an annexe might seem a bit strange, but this is fairly new territory in Britain. Fuelled by soaring house prices and the cost of care in residential homes, the extended family home seems to have arrived in the United Kingdom for good.

When you think about it, the basic facilities of independence do not require a lot of space. A separate entrance door, a shower room with WC, and a lounge/bedroom will do it. And if you want to provide independence from the main home's kitchen, a kitchenette or at least a microwave and sink can be added.

For new homes, there is a tendency to count the reception rooms. To my simple and middle-aged brain, the reception part of a home was the entrance hall and possibly the lounge/family/living room, or whatever else you called it. It is – was – nearest the front door and hence the place you received guests. Now I am led to believe that virtually every room on the entrance level is reception space, including the kitchen. In fact everything except the utility room. The annexe layout should therefore lead you into the living room if you do not have the room to enclose a hallway. Have a good think before you decide it really is not possible. Even when space is tight, it is better to have a hallway or a porch as a place where you can get out of a coat and kick off your shoes. If you do have to open the front door onto a 'reception room', you expose it to draughts and doorstep callers every time it is opened.

Porches are often too small, and the logistics of getting into your home armed with the shopping or the children can be awkward, to say nothing of bringing in new furniture if the doors are at right angles to each other. A small porch can end up being used like an airlock in these situations, where one person at a time has to enter and pass through it. Here it becomes critical that the door width is good enough, and a standard 838-mm (2-ft 9-in) door leaf will be the absolute minimum. The accessibility requirements of the Building Regulations that were introduced for people with disabilities have come to our rescue here because they have effectively done away with the industry standard 762-mm (30-in) door on new homes that had been with us for so long.

What's more, the two-foot-six door was always too narrow for something unless the something could approach it head on. The accessibility standards redeem themselves here, giving elbow room to everyone's life.

Mews and garage annexes

In a mews annexe, you will undoubtedly have to climb the stairs to the next floor to enter the living space proper. Mews annexes are built over a garage or parking space that occupies the footprint at ground level. It pays to have the entrance hall and a cloakroom WC before you climb the stairs and, if you have the luxury of space, a utility/laundry room for the noisy white goods that you do not really want in the kitchen. All else lies on the floor above.

Originally, mews homes were stables designed to house the horse and carriage downstairs, while living space was upstairs. Now they house just the carriage and occupy less of our precious garden space. The word 'mews' literally means an enclosure, or a contained 'built' space. At the end of the twentieth century, we saw mews living as the only design choice for homes in flood-risk areas where bedrooms at ground level were not permitted. In true wetlands, such as those in the southern United States, houses such as this are built on stilts alongside beaches and waterways. Now the architecture is coming back to its roots in cities. But it is not just in cities that we see its comeback. Today, anyone wanting to increase their living space can build over the garage or carport, looking to go up, rather than out.

If you do not need to retain the garage for your car, there is little point in building over it. Instead, you could look to the space within. The basic room needed for ancillary accommodation is often found within the space of a decent garage, and converting one to an annexe can be easy. Garages make ideal annexes if you can connect up the drainage for an en-suite or kitchenette to them, even if some require extending a little. If you do need to make them bigger, take full advantage of the extension by using it to house those 'wet' rooms, and provide the drainage and services to the new part. In some cases, planning permission may not be needed, but when it is, the first consideration is often car parking. An extension for a self-contained annexe can sometimes be a problem if it entirely covers the driveway or converts the garage, unless enough space remains for parking.

Annexes are not separate dwellings, however, and thus have no unconnected value on the open market, where they are regarded no differently to any other addition to the property, at least in terms of value. To put it simply, they cannot be sold off separately.

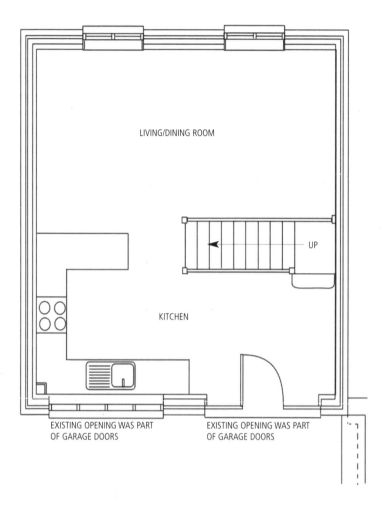

▸ A garage-
to-annexe
conversion.

LIVING/DINING ROOM

UP

KITCHEN

EXISTING OPENING WAS PART
OF GARAGE DOORS

EXISTING OPENING WAS PART
OF GARAGE DOORS

Garage-to-annexe converting

From the late 1960s onwards, many new homes were built with
attached garaging and, almost without exception, the garages are
undersized and underemployed for their intended purpose.
Typically they are 5.5 m long by 2.5 m wide. With around 13 m²
of floor area to form an annexe in, everything has to be kept to a
minimum, much as it does in studio flat design.

The more generously proportioned garages come from the
1960s and earlier. Invariably they are covered by a flat roof, at
least in part, enclosed to feature a garage up-and-over door at the
front and a personnel door at the rear, with brick walls. It soon
made sense for developers building homes with garages attached
to provide an internal door to the house for maximum
convenience. The layout does not offer too much scope for
interior design, but if the rear wall can be divided into two with

some partitioning, a small kitchenette facility can be created by the rear door (which can be retained as the back door) and a small bathroom facility built alongside. The remaining space can then be occupied as a lounge/bedroom area ideal for self-contained teenage life. A student flat would not be much bigger, and these often share kitchen space down the corridor.

Most garages do not have a great storey height and, if the garage has a flat roof, there is nothing you can do about that short of pitching a new roof over it. If it has a pitched roof to start with, it is definitely worth using this roof space and bringing it into the annexe. Raising the ceiling line to the sloping rafters and building in a skylight window will allow much more daylight to bounce around the room and create a feeling of space and airiness that might otherwise be lacking.

Some attached garages are so quickly converted that they can be occupied a few short weeks after the car has been moved out. With cavity walls and a sound floor, the finishings can be done as soon as wall and windows replace the garage doors. Still, even with the structure in place, turning an unoccupied part of the home into living space should not be rushed.

Damp

Even if the garage is structurally dry to begin with, literally a tonne of water could have been used in the finishings and that will take weeks to dry out. Indeed the moisture in fresh plaster and screed usually takes several weeks to come out fully. A damp new residence will not be appreciated, so allow some time and keep the place well ventilated before it is occupied. You can help enormously by using dry finishings, rather than wet ones. Dry-lining walls instead of plastering them, laying chipboard floating floors instead of screeding them – these will speed up the process of occupation.

If you rush the finishes at the end, decorate and occupy the annexe, the risk of mould occurring will be high. I have seen MDF skirting boards, doors and windowsills, along with the corners of plastered walls, covered in black mould inside newly completed annexes. Mould is, of course, a health problem, and living in a home with damp air is not going to do you much good either. By damp, I mean 70 per cent relative humidity or more – fungal spores flourish in these conditions.

As you might imagine, the treatments for mould growth are chemical and unpleasant, and include quaternary ammonium compounds, sodium pentachlorhenate and dichlorophen – chemicals that I am sure are just as unpleasant to live with as the fungus was. This is why you must stop it from appearing in the first place. Extracting humid air from damp rooms such as kitchens and bathrooms is an essential part of this process, and mechanical extractor fans that are automatically triggered by humidistat switches (rather than light switches) are worth installing. They tend to be preset to 65 per cent relative humidity, and hence they do not run when they are not needed. For these fans to work effectively, they should be located above the source of the moisture, whether it be a bath or a sink, and not in a remote part of the room away from the appliances.

External walls

Garages are not all built to the same specification. Some have cavity walls extended from the main house; others have single-leaf brick walls. Some have effective damp proofing and well-constructed roofs – and others do not. The quality of your garage's construction is going to make a big difference to how much work needs to be done to bring it up to standard for living space and compliance with the Building Regulations. If you have the luxury of cavity walls in your garage, make sure that they are insulated. If they are not at present, blown fibreglass can be injected into them to greatly improve their resistance to passing heat.

But let's assume the worst-case scenario first. In this instance, the walls are only a half-brick thickness (113 mm) and the floor has been laid roughly in concrete without a damp-proof membrane. The roof is flat and covered in bitumen felt. The first priority is to make the roof weather-resistant, and that means dry in all weathers.

Creating weather-resistant walls from only single brickwork can be done by damp-proofing the inside of them with a bitumen-based paint or tanking solution, but these products are not usually breathable and could lead to condensation being trapped in the finished structure and unable to disperse. I say the finished structure because it will need to be lined with insulation and boarded out. With the cold face of that insulation on the outside, condensation may form on the tanking, unable to disperse through the membrane. If you do decide to use this method, it is essential to use a vapour-permeable tanking layer to avoid damp from a sweating wall.

If you can afford the space a cavity is really what is needed between the outer face and the new inner and insulated lining, but of course space is rarely in abundance. Normally a 50-mm wide cavity and a 100-mm insulated stud partition would be erected, effectively losing 300 mm in width and length from the floor area.

In these dimension-challenged times, however, the cavity could be cut down, as well as the thickness of the inner leaf. A 25-mm cavity and a 50-mm insulated stud partition will cut the wall thickness in half and still perform the job. The height of the studs, however, will mean that they will benefit from a bit of extra support. At 2.3 m or more between the floor (sole plate) and ceiling (head plate), a 50 x 50 mm stud partition will be a little overstretched for rigidity; some remedial-fix timber-frame wall ties along the centre will tie it in to the brickwork and stiffen it up. Look for stainless-steel twisted ties that you can plug and screw into the wall and nail or screw into the timber. Remedial ties have a dogleg end which is surface-fixed to the masonry, then a twist across the cavity to dislodge any water trying to track across them and a flat end for screwing into the timber. A single row, at mid height across the wall, will be sufficient to support it by effectively cutting the vertical span of the 50 x 50 mm studs in half.

The system requires a level floor on which to sit. If you do not have a level floor, you will need to fix a timber sole plate down first, via some packing shims. The timber has some strength and can be packed out to joists or concrete to get it level. It might seem odd, but a damp-proof course should be installed beneath it, even when you are fixing directly to a new concrete or screed finish that is still drying out.

The short pieces of timber fixed in rows between the studs to also stiffen the wall and provide a fixing point for the plasterboard lining are called noggins.

Insulation and cold bridging

With only 50 mm of insulation thickness available to you, the choice of material is slim – nothing less than rigid sheets of polyurethane or phenolic foam board will cut it. And, speaking of cutting it, wear a face mask when you do. The airborne particles of these petroleum by-product materials are not good to inhale. The great thing about stud walls is that they allow the insulation to be fitted between the studs and in the wall thickness, thus saving space. Alas, this means that it will be in pieces and not continuous, and the studs themselves will represent 'cold bridges' in the wall. Cold bridging is the effect where solid, uninsulated parts of the construction allow heat to pass through.

Metal studs are galvanised and tend to be thinner than timber, and the plasterboard manufacturers promote metal stud systems as an alternative to timber. The metal is thinly pressed lightweight steel and removes some of the cold-bridging effect. Timber might seem like a warm material, but it is not compared to insulation, and overdoing the timber will create too much heat loss through the wall.

The sections of metal are C-shaped in the case of vertical studs, and U-shaped in the head and sole plates, fixed in place by either a twist lock or self-tapping screws. One of the great advantages of metal comes when you reach the top of the sheet and need support for the plasterboard ends. With metal studs, a thin fixing channel is cut and screwed to the stud's face, providing all the support you need for both of the boards joined here.

As greater strength is needed around door and window openings, the C-section studs are then filled or backed up with a timber stud subframe – something to which the door or window frame can be fixed. I do not see metal studs being used in homes very often – hardly at all, in fact. Timber seems to give home improvers the strength and solidity they are looking for, and it is a much more tactile and friendly material with which to work.

You can still drill holes for all your water and electric cables to run through when you use metal studs, as you would with timber, but rubber grommets are needed to line those holes before the services are passed through. These are the same grommets you use in socket boxes after the holes have been punched out to stop the sharp edges chafing the cable insulation.

If you go with timber studs, you can reduce some of the cold-bridging effect by covering the inside with a thin insulation liner (such as multi-laminated aluminium foil sheets), which also can double up as vapour barriers. On the warm inside face of the wall it pays to stop vapour getting through and into the structure. The thin multiple-laminate insulation products are great for lining these stud walls, even if you have insulation in between the studs. They prevent cold bridging through the framework and boost the insulation values of the wall significantly. I have used the aluminium-faced bubble-wrap insulation, but there are several products around. The insulation value of some has been in question for many years and unfortunately the subject of a lengthy trade war between leading manufacturers in this industry. It is all to do with the method of testing the product to arrive at its insulation qualities. In 2006, a revision in the Building Regulation guidance on thermal insulation made it clearer just how these products should be tested to arrive at their performance. All of which means they are ideal for backing up other thicker insulation products, but not so good alone, which is what some of the manufacturers were pitching their sales and price on.

Three examples of internal linings to a single-skin garage wall

113-mm brick outer leaf
50-mm cavity
100-mm studwork with 100-mm rigid mineral-fibre sheets
between the studs
Foil multi-laminate insulation sheet
9.5-mm plasterboard and plaster finish

113-mm brick outer leaf
25-mm cavity
75-mm studwork with 75-mm rigid polyurethane foam boards
between the studs
9.5-mm plasterboard and plaster finish

113-mm brick outer leaf
25-mm cavity
50-mm studwork with 50-mm rigid phenolic foam boards
between the studs
Foil multi-laminate insulation sheet
9.5-mm plasterboard and plaster finish

External insulation and cladding

Keeping the loss of floor space to the minimum will be essential
when converting to an annexe, but you might be able to avoid
any loss of floor space entirely if you instead work on the outside
of the wall to insulate and weather it. A cladding system of wall
boarding, render or tile hanging will achieve this but it will need
to extend down to the floor structure level. The insulation is fixed
first to the outside of the wall and will be at least 50 mm thick.
This, together with the cladding, will reposition the fascia line.

Entrance doors

The beauty and indeed the point of an annexe is that it has its
own entrance door, and consumer power has won when it comes
to the door itself. What we like is what we get. Georgian colours
of deep red, blue or green in a high-gloss finish, decorated with
shiny brass ironmongery. Classic looks. As much as we do not like
painting, we like PVC-u front doors even less. Most home
builders know this. Manufacturers do not seem to have got the
proportions for plastic doors right, and only by making them
bigger does this seem possible.

Plastic, you see, is not as strong as wood and, to make up for
its lack of strength, it has to be thicker. The chunkiness does not

stop at the frame – even the average door leaf itself tends to look short and squat in PVC-u. The mouldings, such as they are in that cellular stuff, lack edges and style compared to a solid wood door, and the sill at the bottom has to be ascended with some enthusiasm. If you happen to be elderly, infirm or just lazy, you are going to fall over it every time. Plastic doors sit in plastic frames that are designed to an equal width on all four sides, with only weather resistance in mind. Not only do they keep the weather out, but they nearly keep us out as well. It takes some skill and agility to get over the high doorsill without stumbling, let alone having to deal with it from a wheelchair.

On 25 October 1999, the government introduced a new requirement in England and Wales – under access for new dwellings – that directly affected the front door. It did away with thresholds and doorsteps, and made doors accessible for wheelchair users, parents with buggies and the elderly. The requirement had gone through a long and turbulent period of drafting and consultation, during which the house builders had lobbied enthusiastically against it, but from that day it became law. As it happens, the annexe is not a 'new dwelling' under the requirement, and hence its entrance door need not comply with it, but it is worth making this door as access-friendly as you can in any case. New entrance doors are now made with accessible thresholds as standard, so all you need to do is to protect it from the elements.

At the time of the new requirement's birth, *The Times* newspaper covered its arrival with an article entitled 'The death of the British doorstep', or something along those lines. The angle of the piece, as you might gather, was that something distinctly British and well loved was being done away with. It was a conservation-minded bit of journalism, I suppose, but it is a fact that the doorstep had a purpose beyond providing a platform on which milk bottles could sit. It kept the rain out. Without a doorstep, the wind could blow it straight under the door to puddle on the floor inside.

To counteract this, the law makers provided guidance on fitting flush-level drainage channels and sheltering the door with a canopy, absolutely none of which assuaged the house builders. I have no doubt that there are homes dotted around the country where people have to mop the floor behind the front door after every occluded front passes through, but for the most part the drains seem to work. I suppose that it is all a matter of extreme, but it seems to me that, if the rainwater is slamming into the door on the seat of a southwesterly gale, the water running down it could easily be pushed underneath when it reaches the bottom. The great British doorstep would not have helped you here, but the water bar that was embedded in the sill would have. That little metal bar was enough to save getting the mop out, but the new breed of accessible thresholds does not have it because it can be extremely difficult for a wheelchair user to get over. What is far more effective, therefore, is to locate the door on a sheltered wall or beneath an overhanging roof.

A canopy roof or porch shelter is a very nice feature to have on your annexe, and with good reason – as long as it has a gutter. Small roofs such as this often do not, as they do not collect enough rainwater to warrant it being piped away into the drains. Many builders do not bother fitting rainwater goods to them, but when you are standing outside on a rainy night, you are going to wish that they had. These tiny roofs are just about perfectly sized so that any run-off will trickle down the back of your neck as you stand fumbling with the keys in the half-light of the porch lantern for too long.

Composite doors

Manufacturers have at last recognised the pros and cons of timber and plastic doors, creating the 'composite' door, which is a hybrid of the two. With the strength of a timber core, the composite door is faced with metal and a durable polymer coating that requires no redecoration. It is usually imprinted with a timber grain and available in traditional front-door colours, as well as white. The coating is factory-sprayed to the door's thin metal facing. These doors are soft-faced and easily dented, but they can be filled and redecorated.

Security

With a third of a million attempted burglaries every year in the United Kingdom, security is a prime consideration. The new generation of burglars possesses tools for attacking the lock cylinders and pulling them clean out. With external handles and locks being attacked, additional features are needed to keep the annexe secure. Of course, you can have as many bolts and locks as you like, but, if you forget to engage them, they will not help much. Sadly, in most cases of reported burglary, entry has been through an unlocked or unsecured window or door. Burglars are opportunists, and they are happy to comb an area looking for windows and doors that may have been left vulnerable. When it is locked, your annexe front door should boast standard equipment, including it being hung on three 100-mm long hinges. If the pins are vulnerable, hinge bolts should be fitted to the frame to stop the door being lifted off the hinges. A key-operated (with at least a thousand differs) automatic dead lock that is fixed so well that you could not get it out without busting the doorframe along with it is also essential. Make sure that it has a bolt of hardened steel that cannot be sawn through, but also a simple lever action on the inside to release it so you can get out in a hurry if the need arises. Restraint arms are favoured over security chains as standard now (they do the same job), and any spy-hole in the door should be at about 1.5 m high, so that you can see if those really are carol singers standing on your doorstep. Secondary locks are often fitted on the line of the middle rail, half-way down, and these should be at least 600 mm away from the primary lock.

Although the armoury on doors has improved, the detail remains pretty much the same as it always has for wooden models – 44 mm thick dividing up thinner panels. The panels are the door's Achilles heel when it comes to security, as they are more easily kicked in; however, if they are narrow and small as they should be, this should not be enough to gain entry. Glass panels that can be cut more quietly have also to be located out of reach of the locks for the longest of arms.

In truth, not many burglars are daft enough to try busting in through the front door in full view of the neighbours. They much prefer to skulk around the back, where they can work out of sight.

Thermal Comfort

What passes as comfortable for one person may not for another, but for most of us the same factors should prevail to achieve the perfect environment indoors.

◆ The relative humidity should be between 40 and 60 per cent, so that the air is neither too dry nor too damp.
◆ There should be some horizontal gentle air flow passing over us between 0.2 and 0.25 m/sec from background ventilation.
◆ The air temperature should be somewhere between 18°C and 24°C.
◆ The air around our feet should not be more than 3°C less than the air around our head.

Thermostatic radiator valves by themselves will control the flow of water into radiators and even, set to zero, turn themselves 'off' unless a frost risk occurs, but they will not stop the boiler from cycling by themselves. They have no electronic connection to the boiler, and consequently they cannot shut it down when heat is not required. This is why a room thermostat is a far better option. A room thermostat creates a zone in the annexe that can instruct the boiler when to send in hot water to heat it and when it is warm enough to shut the boiler off if no other demands are being place upon it. Only two thin wires are required between a room thermostat and the boiler itself if it is hardwired onto a wall. Wireless room thermostats exist that can be transported about, but in my experience they simply add to the moveable clutter and get themselves lost. Better to fix the thermostat to the lounge wall, where its presence can be relied upon.

It is the industry standard to work to an internal design temperature of 21°C in living rooms and bathrooms, and 18°C in bedrooms, cloakrooms and hallways, but the annexe is likely to be a single zone. This means it is best to use intelligent thermostats that have programmable temperature settings throughout the day. Some of these have an external sensor that can respond to changes in the outside temperature and compensate accordingly; others have the ability to learn how long it takes the room to reach the desired temperature and delay the start-up time accordingly. These optimum-start controls can save fuel and cut costs, making them excellent energy-saving devices.

Heating

By far the most economical and easily achieved option with an annexe is to extend the main home's heating system, as a separate zone with its own controls. If there is a downside to this, it is that both occupancies will be using the same boiler for heating water and some apportioning of the fuel bill may have to take place based on the ratio of floor area. Obviously, the better you insulate the annexe, the less heating will be required and, with a small space such as this, it is not impossible to reduce the heating demand to an absolute minimum. Good insulation will also keep it cool in summer

There is no reason why a carefully designed small space cannot be attractive and functional, even when it comes to heating it and providing hot water.

No room for radiators

Underfloor heating will remove the need for radiators that impinge on floor space and where your furniture can go, and so that, too, becomes essential and it, too, can run as an extension of your existing central heating, but isolated from the central heating in the main house. This means that the boiler can be shut down when the main house is empty and the annexe still occupied. It is possible to use manifold kits that create an additional heating zone for the annexe from the circuit for the main home. The hot-water supply will be provided from the boiler in the main home (and hence you might have to divide out the cost of fuel on a floor area percentage for the annexe), but otherwise the controls allow it to be isolated and the floor heated independently.

If you would prefer the resident to experience more independence (for this read: pay their own fuel bill), a small electric boiler is the most convenient to install. You could still use an underfloor wet heating system, but instead of a standard manifold with pump and thermostatic valve, a tiny electric boiler (eg 2-kw model) can be fitted instead of the manifold. These, the smallest of boiler units, typically occupy a space less than 600 mm high and 300 mm wide, and can be hidden away in a cupboard (like an undersink kitchen unit), as they require no flue or ventilation.

Small electric boiler systems are unvented sealed systems, and you will also need to find room for a pressure expansion vessel (see the illustration on page 130), which is slightly bulkier. Floor areas of up to 20 m² can be heated by a 2-kw model fed from a small expansion tank and fitted with a programmer and a room thermostatic control, and this will achieve independence from the main home's heating. These are ideal for detached annexes because, unless your annexe is within a few short metres of the main home, it will need an independent heating and hot-water system.

Although I have seldom seen it done, heating a detached annexe by extending a hot-water supply pipe out to it is theoretically possible if the pipe is fully protected and well insulated. The potential heat loss and risk of freezing mean that it would need to be buried underground in a suitable duct. A 100-mm below-ground drainage pipe would be ideal for this, as it has the robustness and resistance for the job. All that remains is to insulate the hot-water pipe before feeding it through the duct with pre-formed foam pipe lagging. Using plastic pipe will help enormously because it does not suffer from the same heat losses as copper, it is cheaper and, most importantly, it can be laid out in one length, joint-free. As it is a supply pipe to feed a separate and remote zone on the system, flow rates have to be considered, and a 22-mm pipe will be much better than a 15-mm one.

PIPE LENGTHS NEEDED FOR ANNEXE FLOOR AREA	
100-mm spacing	8.2 m length per square metre of floor area
200-mm spacing	4.5 m of length per square metre of floor area
300-mm spacing	3.1 m of length per square metre of floor area

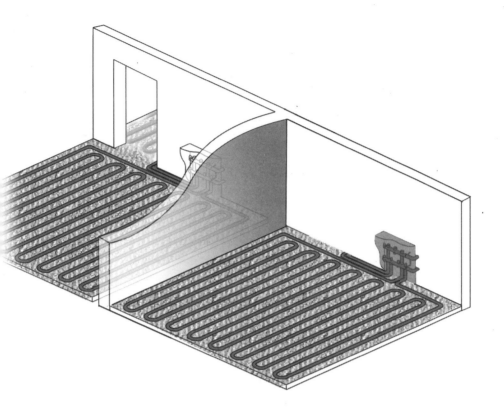

The question of the depth of this supply really hinges on the conditions in your location, but treating it as you would the cold-water supply mean that you will not go far wrong. At 600 mm below ground, the temperature is surprisingly stable and, on frosty winter mornings, a below-ground hot-water pipe encased in lagged ducting will fare much better than one in an unheated garage.

▲ Some wall or cupboard space is needed for the manifold control valves and pump for underfloor wet heating systems.

Underfloor wet systems
Underfloor heating uses the floor itself as a radiator, avoiding the need to hang steel panels on the walls. As it is larger than these conventional radiators, it can be heated to a lower temperature to achieve the same result. For towel warming, a conventional bathroom towel radiator may still be installed to the system.

Once laid in position, what appears as a network of plastic (polybutylene) pipes on the floor is quite often just one pipe in a small annexe – one pipe that does a circuit of the floor and is flexible enough to bend to the radii of the supporting clips or pro-forma and be joint-free. These systems are very reliable because they are jointless when they are buried beneath the floor finishings and are consequently unlikely to leak. The 25-year guarantee offered by installers may be discarded if a pipe has to be cut and joined to extend a circuit, for example, so it pays to get the design right from the beginning.

Originally intended for solid floors, underfloor wet systems are available now for suspended timber floors as well. Insulation between the floor joists and under the pipes is a prerequisite, but after that the pipes can be laid into retainer plates that are recessed between the joists and can be boarded over. Of all the systems available, the ones that use a cut-out retainer tray to hold the pipework in place are so much quicker to install. With these, the pipe is literally walked into the retaining grooves, and there is none of that mucking about with clips to try to hold it down. As with sprinkler systems, underfloor heating pipework can run only for a limited length in a circuit – about 100 m – because of the pressure loss. If that distance seems a lot, remember that the a pipe is laid in a grille pattern and, at 100 mm separation, that amounts to one circuit supplying a room of 11 m². If you can widen the pipe spacing to 200 mm on the grille, then obviously you can double that area. A single circuit at the greater spacing could supply an open-plan apartment, or you might prefer to break it into zones of separate circuits for separate thermal controls.

▸ Manifolds can be used to create a separate heating zone in the annexe.

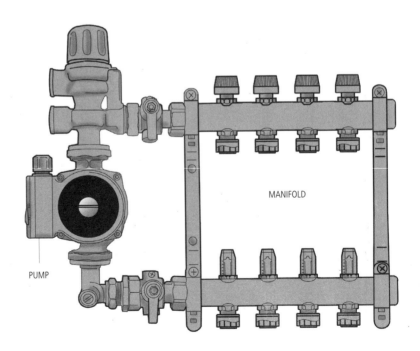

MANIFOLD

PUMP

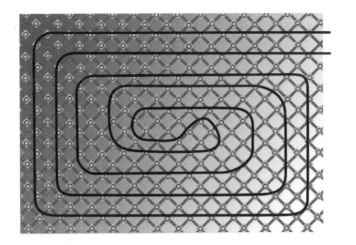

◀ Pre-formed tray to support pipes.

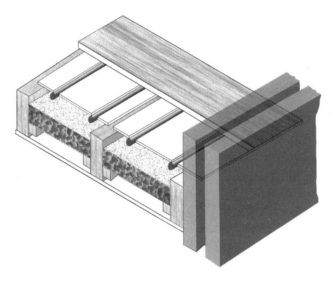

◀ Underfloor heating pipes can be laid on trays over wooden joists...

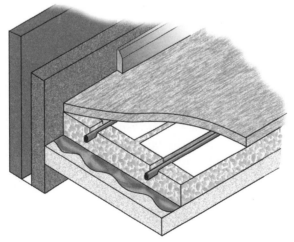

◀ ...or in insulation trays over concrete floors with floor finishings over them.

Generally, the hallways or lobbies are connected to the room circuits and will not have a separate circuit of their own. Once you know how many circuits you will have, a manifold can be selected with the exact number of ports needed to link them together.

The new-build annexe

If you are not blessed with a garage to convert, building your annexe from scratch as an extension or a detached building is not such a bad alternative. You will be able to plan the layout exactly to meet your needs and not scrimp on space or facilities. Although some extensions as 'permitted development' do not require planning permission, when it is needed, planners often consider the self-contained annexe more favourably where it is needed to house a dependent relative.

▾ New-build annexe foundations will need to be excavated to an approved depth dependent on the ground conditions and building load.

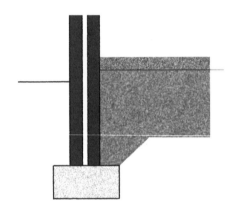

Foundations

The depth of annexe foundations may not be any different to those of a new dwelling. It is all about the subsoil on which the foundations will be placed. Foundations formed in rock and stony ground can often be shallower than those dug in shrinkable soils such as clay. In the latter, at least 1 m deep is usual, but nearby trees or shrubs may extend this depth to a good deal more. Your building control officer will guide you in these cases. Once the trenches have been dug and inspected, you will need to hammer pegs into the sides to mark the level for the top of the concrete. Timber pegs are safer than steel pins.

Traditionally, about 300 mm thick and 600 mm wide strip foundations conserve concrete. If you have a sloping site, you will need to step the foundations to keep them level. Steps should overlap at least the width of the trench when concreted, and that means shuttering across them. Use plywood and retaining pegs. Strip foundations are often necessary in softer soils such as sand, as they spread the load of the building out over a greater area.

Trench fill foundations avoid bricklaying below ground. The concrete is poured to within 150 mm of the surface ground level, saving time and trouble.

A raft foundation may be a better alternative, as it provides the base for the floor as well, but rafts need to be suitably designed by structural engineers. Sheets of steel mesh reinforcement are laid

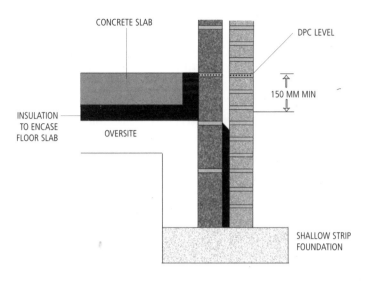

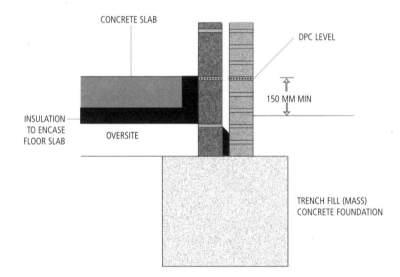

◄ The two main choices for foundation types are strip and trench-fill.

out over the whole footprint of the annexe, and these will be tied to edge beams beneath the walls. The edge beams themselves may be reinforced with straight bars of steel, forming a cage within a shallow trench.

Floor structure

Where a raft is not used, the floor structure will have to be formed independently. The ground beneath a ground-bearing

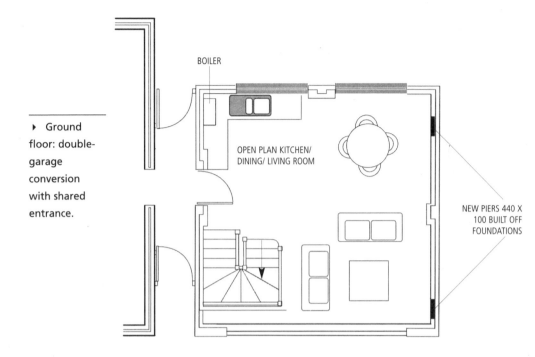

▸ Ground floor: double-garage conversion with shared entrance.

BOILER

OPEN PLAN KITCHEN/ DINING/ LIVING ROOM

NEW PIERS 440 X 100 BUILT OFF FOUNDATIONS

GROUND FLOOR PLAN

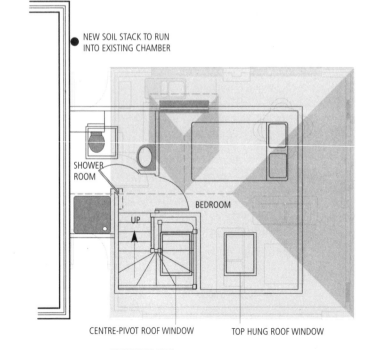

▸ First floor: roof conversion to form first floor with new dormer and skylight windows.

NEW SOIL STACK TO RUN INTO EXISTING CHAMBER

SHOWER ROOM

BEDROOM

UP

CENTRE-PIVOT ROOF WINDOW

TOP HUNG ROOF WINDOW

FIRST FLOOR PLAN

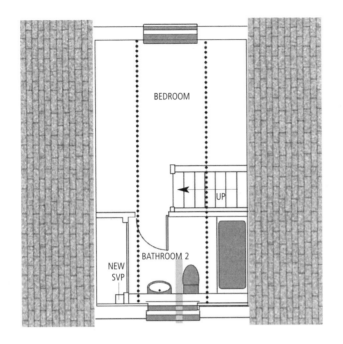

◄ First-floor: alternative garage conversion with gabled windows.

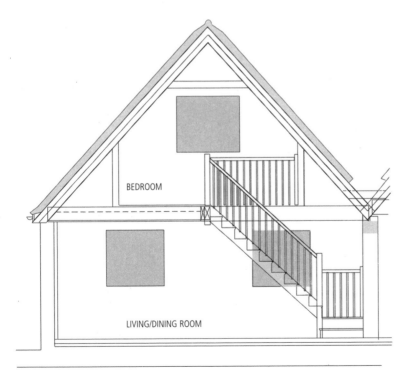

◄ A cross-section through both floors.

concrete floor slab must be properly prepared with an oversite treatment from the reduced ground level. This infill construction of hardcore rubble should be at least 150 mm thick (but no greater than 600 mm) and consist of selected aggregate, compacted in layers with a plate compactor. If this task is done badly or with the wrong material, settlement is to be expected, which will cause the slab to crack later on.

Check out your options for oversite material locally. Hardcore rubble is a good recycled material to use, but it needs to be clean. Broken or crushed brick, concrete or stone that has been supplied should be less than 100 mm in particle size. On sloping sites where part of the oversite may exceed 600 mm deep, it may be acceptable to use lean-mix concrete in layers with the hardcore to make up the difference, instead of switching to a suspended floor type such as timber or precast concrete joists.

Lap and tape down 1200-gauge polythene for the damp-proof membrane, and make sure that it is dressed up over the walls so that it can later be lapped with the damp-proof course before concreting. After placing the concrete, the hard work is in raking it out and tamping it into level using a straight length of timber that will span across from the walls on either side. Tamping the concrete helps to consolidate it in the same way that vibrating it does, and a gentle sawing and tapping motion will bring the surface to the level and finish needed to seat the insulation. Once

▶ The damp-
proof
membrane
should be
lapped to the
damp-proof
course (DPC) in
the wall.

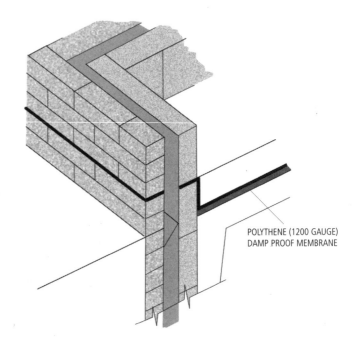

POLYTHENE (1200 GAUGE)
DAMP PROOF MEMBRANE

the concrete is set, the insulation boards can be laid over the concrete slab beneath the floor finishing. It is best to use phenolic foam boards 75–100 mm thick.

Drainage

Trenches need to be carefully dug to the right depth and gradient to avoid huge amounts of bedding being necessary to support the pipes. Gravel is used for both bedding and surround material supporting and protecting the pipes at the correct fall. A gradient of 1:40 is ideal, but plastic drains will tolerate much shallower falls if it becomes necessary.

◆ Lay pipes to an even gradient.
◆ Lay pipes in straight lines and avoid bends.
◆ Locate the soil vent pipe at the head of the run.
◆ Provide rodding points or inspection chambers at bends and changes in gradient.

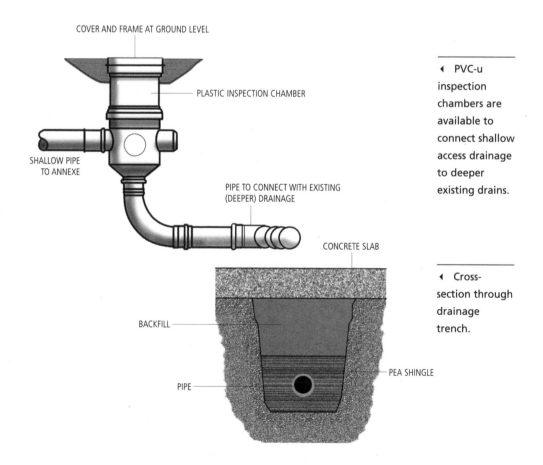

COVER AND FRAME AT GROUND LEVEL

PLASTIC INSPECTION CHAMBER

SHALLOW PIPE TO ANNEXE

PIPE TO CONNECT WITH EXISTING (DEEPER) DRAINAGE

CONCRETE SLAB

BACKFILL

PEA SHINGLE

PIPE

◀ PVC-u inspection chambers are available to connect shallow access drainage to deeper existing drains.

◀ Cross-section through drainage trench.

◆ Connect WCs and soil vent pipes direct to inspection chambers rather than Y junctions.
◆ Use at least 100 mm of gravel to cover the pipes before backfilling the trench.

External walls

With the damp-proof course bedded, the external walls can be raised. Building in masonry cavity construction will mean starting with the outer leaf of face brickwork. The mortar joints should be of equal thickness in every course and of equal width in the vertical joints ('perp' ends). A good-quality appearance is everything when it comes to face brickwork. The following five points are key to achieving this.

1. The brickwork should rise 300 mm in four courses and the 'perp' ends line up in alternate courses.
2. Gauge rods should be used to keep the wall vertical and equally coursed.
3. The brickwork should not be raised more than 1200 mm above any adjacent work in one laying.
4. It should be protected overnight against frost and snow with hessian sheets.
5. The sand must be kept clean (by covering it on site or having it delivered in 1-tonne bags).

Cavities are best closed at the edges of windows and door openings with preformed insulated cavity closures. These plastic foam–filled closers also act as vertical damp-proof courses.

CAVITY WALL TIE SPACINGS			
Cavity width	Maximum centres		Number of ties per
	Vertical	Horizontal	square metre of wall
76–100 mm	750 mm	450 mm	3.0
101–150 mm	450 mm	450 mm	4.9

Cavity wall insulation

Today, insulation adds at least 100 mm to the thickness of an external wall. Whether you use a total (100 mm) mineral wool fill cavity or a partial-fill (50 mm) polyurethane foam board may depend upon the degree of exposure to wind-driven rain. A skin of brickwork (112 mm thick) can leak dramatically when the rain is pushed in by wind pressure, and cavity wall insulation products are treated with water repellent to avoid them absorbing it. The water should drain down the face and out through the foundations, or weep from holes above damp-proof course level.

The insulation batts should be cleanly inserted and butted together, without any mortar dropping between them. Keeping them clean and dry is a challenge on some sites. Avoid them being wedged or forced into gaps or left exposed at the top in wet weather. If water gets a chance, it will track across the gaps between the batts and soak down into them until they are saturated. From there on, it is inevitable that damp will find its way through the inner leaf and into your home. Using a board to keep the cavity clear of mortar as work proceeds will help a lot. The same applies to partial-fill insulation, which relies on retaining a 50-mm clear cavity on the outer face. If you have any concerns about the exposure of the walls and the standard of workmanship, you might prefer to use a cladding system over blockwork on the outside.

Inner leaf of cavity walls

Lightweight blocks are the traditional inner leaf and help with the thermal insulation which means having to be careful about the ones you use, the lightest are best thermally but poor for fixing things to the walls – like kitchen cupboards. Blocks should be cut as necessary beneath around openings and plates and not replaced by bricks. Using bricks will produce a cold bridge for heat to transfer through even if your cavity is insulated, so it is essential to cut blocks to fit. If you are building the wall yourself you might want to look at using the thin joint system which is easier to keep level and vertical. Thin jointing uses adhesive to bond them together rather than mortar. Block manufacturers will guide you with advice on how to use their system.

Lateral restraint

Your roof and any upper floors (but not the ground floor) are required to offer lateral support to the external walls, and this is done with steel restraint straps tying the two together. The straps are installed perpendicular to the rafters and joists at a maximum spacing of 2 m, and either side of openings for doors and windows wherever you have a wall longer than 3 m.

Timber-framed construction

In house building, timber-framed construction usually consists of a studwork frame inner leaf as the structural element replacing the blockwork, and a masonry outer leaf as a rain shield, with a cavity between. Quite often it is brickwork. The structure is quicker to erect up to the point where it can be weathered in and the outer wall has to be built. Once it is and the roof is tiled, the insulation is fitted between the timber studs of the framework and because of this it can be considerably thick and yet still maintain a clear cavity for weather resistance. A 140-mm deep stud is now used to achieve the insulation standard. The frame is braced, with a lining of plywood or OSB sheathing to provide resistance to racking movement under wind load. The walls are made off site in panels and erected into position by crane, and you can expect to hire one for a couple of days to get all the walls up and the roof trusses on. The sole plates of timber-framed walls need securing down without damaging the damp-proof course and, to achieve this, special anchor plates are used which allow the plate to be fixed to the ground floor rather than the wall substructure.

Sheathing is covered with a breathable membrane, which adds some weather resistance behind the cladding. The membrane is usually stapled to the sheathing and needs to be well lapped at joints.

Quality checks for a good timber-framed construction
1. Check that foundations have been accurately set out – within plus or minus 10 mm per 6 m length of wall.
2. Check floors and walls below the sole plates are level to plus or minus 6 mm in 6-m intervals, and take great care in levelling beneath base plates with shims and a dry-packed mortar bed.
3. Secure sole plates using metal angles rather than fixing down through the damp-proof course.
4. Do not allow the wall panels to be moved out of plumb to accept incorrectly made trusses or beams.
5. Avoid gaps and inadequate fixing between wall panels.
6. Check that the upper floor wall panels are nailed securely to floor joists and are packed out beneath properly between the joists.
7. Make sure that the outer breather membrane overlaps the sole plate and the damp-proof course beneath it is lapped up the inside of the plate to protect it from wet floor finishes (ie screed).
8. If you have timber floors, protect the chipboard floor decking from the elements by using boarding that comes prelaminated with removable film protection.

Single-leaf timber frame buildings

The very same construction used in the internal leaf of traditional timber-frame cavity walls can be used in single-leaf building. It provides all the strength, insulation and internal finishings. All that is missing is weather resistance, and for that a cavity and a brick wall are not essential. Granted, a masonry skin will offer the most security and robustness of all cladding systems, but those are not regulatory functional requirements. Keeping the weather out can be done with timber boarding, PVC-u cladding, rendering or hanging tiles – all of which can be fixed directly to the timber frame.

We tend not to like single-leaf buildings in the United Kingdom, but in North America and Australia they are the standard method of construction for homes. Quick to build and quick to occupy, a dry-build construction of timber with a dry cladding of your choice is ideal for a detached garden annexe.

You can increase the quality of the building by using extra care beneath the finishings, such as using polythene or aluminium laminated foil over the whole timber frame and insulation before you plasterboard. Doing this kind of vapour-sealing work will ensure that you keep annexe-generated moisture out of the structure, but also that you keep bugs and unwelcome visitors from finding a way in. A quality vapour-permeable breather paper over the outside sheathing will also help.

If this construction has a weakness, it is around the openings for windows and doors. Make sure that all the service entry points are through the ground and entering via the floor slab, not the walls, but pay plenty of attention to the structure and

MAXIMUM SPANS FOR RAFTERS

Rafter Size	Maximum span	
	(measured along rafter between supports)	
(C16 or SC3 grade)	Roof pitches from	Roof pitches from
	22.5°–30°	31°–45°
Spacing at	400 mm–600 mm	400 mm–600 mm
50 x 100 mm	2.45 m–2.14 m	2.53 m–2.21 m
50 x 125 mm	3.05 m–2.67 m	3.15 m–2.76 m
50 x 150 mm	3.65 m–3.20 m	3.76 m–3.30 m

- The span of the rafters in the tables is measured along the roof slope.
- 0.6 Kn/sq.m (approx. 600 mm depth of snow) is allowed for snow load. If your annexe is more than 100 m above sea level or if you just want to allow for the next ice age, the figure is upped to 1.0 Kn/sq.m. Also, you should read the spans for one depth of section size less, ie for 50 x 150 read for 50 x 125.

cladding around these bigger openings. You can use a vertical damp-proof course pinned between the windows and studs' adjacent openings, but wide enough to wrap around the front and cover the gap between the two. The cladding will cover it, but it will remain as seal against wind-driven rain when the timber dries and shrinks back. You cannot rely on mastic sealant as the only precaution, but obviously it can be used to finish these details off.

If you do select timber boarding on the outside, there are some limitations that will apply. Timber offers no fire-resistance to the external structure and consequently it is at risk from fire spread when near to other buildings. The minimum distance from the boundary for a timber annexe such as this is 12.5 m, and that can be a problem in all but the largest of gardens. You can reduce the distance by cladding the outside of the timber frame with moisture-resistant plasterboard before you fix the sheathing and breathable paper. I have used this method myself to encase the stud frame in plasterboard inside and out – protecting it from fire on both sides.

Roof structure

For most detached annexes, a pitched roof will not only look better, but also provide some extra valuable space. I would encourage you to look towards a traditional cut-and-pitched roof rather than trussed rafters. The latter are really only economic for larger buildings where the roof space is not needed for anything but insulation and light storage. Once upon a time, all roofs were made this way. The tables shown here look at the maximum spans for various sections in C16 grade and C24 grade softwood.

Ceiling joists

A simple triangle is the best way to form a roof structure, with the rafters of equal length on both sides tied back by the ceiling joists.

MAXIMUM SPANS FOR FLAT ROOF JOISTS		
Size of joist	Maximum span	
	(measured between supports)	
(C16 or SC3 grade)	at 400-mm spacing	at 600-mm spacing
50 x 125 mm	2.53 m	2.37 m
50 x 150 mm	3.19 m	2.97 m
50 x 175 mm	3.81 m	3.47 m
50 x 200 mm	4.48 m	3.97 m
50 x 225 mm	5.09 m	4.47 m

Over large spans, the ceiling joists are better bolted to the rafter feet than nailed to maintain the tie. Although this restraining task places only horizontal load on them and a small 50 x 100 section is adequate for it, the ceiling and access to it also place vertical load. This is often underestimated and the table should be used for sizing where access is proposed.

MAXIMUM SPANS FOR CEILING JOISTS		
Size of joist	Maximum span	
	(measured between supports)	
(C16 OR SC3 grade)	at 400-mm spacing	at 600-mm spacing
50 x 100 mm	1.84 m	1.73 m
50 x 125 mm	2.47 m	2.31 m
50 x 150 mm	3.11 m	2.90 m
50 x 175 mm	3.72 m	3.44 m
50 x 200 mm	4.37 m	4.04 m

Flat roofs are not so economical to build today. The insulation requirement has meant that expensive and thick phenolic foam boards have to be used with the decking, before they can be felted. Flat roofing in the traditional three-layer system is still an option, but it is often badly laid and hence short-lived. The first task is to size the joists correctly.

With furring pieces fixed to allow plenty of fall to keep the rainwater off, the insulation boards can then be fixed down. They require long helical screw fixings to anchor them down and noggins beneath the joints to support the ends. With the decking layer over the insulation, the weathering felts can be laid, starting with a breathable bottom layer. Top layers can be mineralised to avoid the need for bedding loose chipping, or solar-reflective coatings can sometimes be applied. These are silver or white, and highly reflective (which means that you do not want to be looking down on them from nearby upper floors), and most are solvent-based and cannot be used within 6 m of the boundary due to the risk of fire spread.

Log cabin annexe

In the system-build approaches, one genre stands out as ideal for an instant annexe. The log cabin kit builds used in Scandinavia and North America make for attractive natural buildings. In the northern countries of the Baltic, these constructions are the norm for rural homes and are used well inside the Arctic Circle. Indeed, in Norway, they meet the thermal standards for energy efficiency,

where the solid timber alone is considered to have some thermal mass without any additional insulation. I have looked at approving solid wood log cabins for use in the United Kingdom, but here the climate is different and we calculate heat loss in a different way. An additional layer of insulation is needed to make them comply. The beauty of these buildings is in the wood. Lining the inside of them with insulation and plasterboard could be done, but it would not be appreciated – aesthetically or financially.

The only log cabins that meet the United Kingdom's energy-efficiency standards are those that have a cavity between the split logs that can be filled with insulation. Cellulose is the favoured material because it can be blown in wet, but dries to a breathable material. Cellulose is made from recycled newspaper that is mashed up and treated with a fire retardant; it has to be injected by approved installers and needs certification. A cavity width of 75 mm to 100 mm is likely to be needed, and vertical logs separating the exposed split log faces form this. There is no external or internal cladding to be done – the structure is the finished article and ready to be wired, plumbed and occupied.

This is fast-track building, and only a few short weeks separate the commencement of the work from the completion. A heating system fed by an electric boiler and backed up with a log burner for a cheaper and more ecu-friendly form of space heating would be ideal.

It is tempting to think of these log buildings as deluxe sheds, but in every respect they are robust and sustainable buildings. They need foundations to support them and roof coverings to weather them that are no different to those of a traditionally built house. Although they have benefits in appearance and speed of construction, when it comes to fitting them out with electrical installations, bathrooms and kitchens, they can be slower and harder to accommodate. The log-face external walls are best kept free of fixtures and fittings on the inside. Instead you might be able to adapt the kit with some hollow timber stud partitions erected as internal room dividers to facilitate the 'fit-out'. You can then tone down some of that bare wood with some plasterboard and plaster finishing. This will depend on the size of the annexe and whether any of those internal walls are needed as structural buttresses to the external walls, so discuss it with your supplier.

Extending services

For the most part, services such as water and electricity can be easily extended to the detached annexe, buried underground and routed out from the main home. Using deep drainage trenches for running in the other services makes good sense. Gas, electric and water cables all have to be provided at your expense, so laying them in position at this stage will save time and money later.

What can often decide whether an existing detached building is convertible is the provision of drainage. Drains do not need to be serving the building at present, but its floor level does need to be above the drainage system that does exist, once the fall of the pipe has been taken into account. It can sometimes be almost impossible to guess this with the eye; what is really needed is a level. (Levels were once expensive instruments for the professional, but with the advent of laser levels it is possible to buy a relatively inexpensive one and transfer datum accurately from one point to another.) If you allow for a fall of 1:50 from the invert depth of your point of connection to the existing drains (ideally a manhole), you can calculate the level at which your drain needs to begin. A fall of 1:50 is actually not bad for a 100-mm diameter plastic pipe. Indeed, the manufacturers believe that you can go to a much lower gradient (down towards 1:80), but that makes no allowance for ground movement and, in much of the country, the ground moves with the seasons.

▾ Stub stack with rodding access used to connect new plumbing to vented drains.

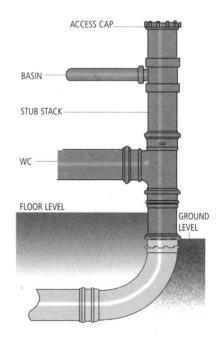

ACCESS CAP

BASIN

STUB STACK

WC

FLOOR LEVEL

GROUND LEVEL

Connecting drainage

In extending your home's drainage system to serve the annexe you will have to deal with existing levels – not only the fixed invert level of the existing drainage pipes, but also the floor level of the new annexe, which determines the drainage entry points of soil vent pipes and gullies. You cannot do anything about the former, and the latter can be tweaked only in the conversion work, and it often happens that the drains rise up to become very shallow in achieving the essential falls.

Shallow drains cannot lie just below the surface as targets waiting for the fork or spade to arrive by accident one day; they have to be protected. They also need some frost protection, which is why you should aim to keep the runs beneath pathways and patios where that protection exists. If that is not possible, backfilling the trench with concrete as a bed, surround and cover will be an acceptable alternative, as long as you provide flexible movement at the joints between pipes and fittings. For the most part, concrete encasing such as this, which will also protect pipes from active tree roots, is best left to clay pipes. Plastic (PVC-u) systems are designed to be very flexible and do not enjoy concrete boots. For them, a capping of reinforced concrete will be better, as it leaves the pipes entirely flexible beneath.

If being too shallow is not your problem, being too deep might be. Depth is not such a great trait for drainage. For one thing, it makes drains difficult to get at when they become blocked and, for another, it is harder to install at depths of more than a metre. Under these conditions, the pipe trenches have to be wider for ground workers to get into and the sides shored up to avoid them collapsing. In addition, you cannot excavate trenches too close to your building without running the risk of undermining the foundations.

Drains do not have to pass beneath the foundations to undermine them; they could simply fall within the 45-degree spread of load from their base corners. If this happens, the pipe and indeed the trench that sits within the undermining zone (see the illustration on page 000) will have to be concreted to at least 150 mm above this level. Not doing so places the foundations at risk of subsidence through the loss of supporting ground. It is actually far less problematic if drains do not run parallel with the foundation walls of homes and their annexes.

Septic tanks

When it simply is not possible to get a connection to the existing drainage system, the annexe could be served by a small septic

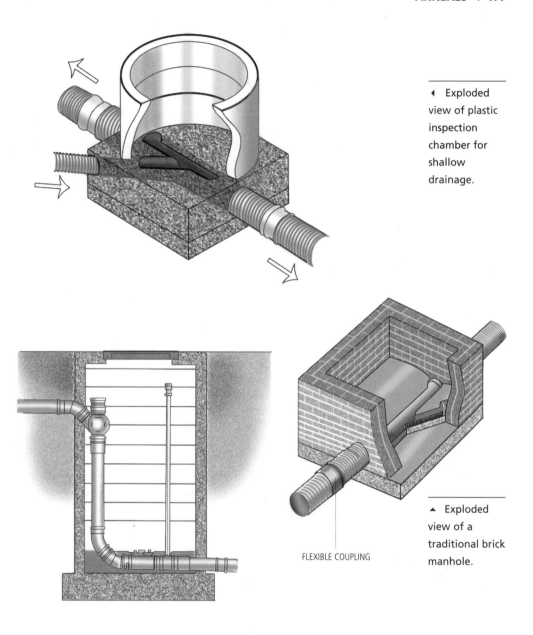

◀ Exploded view of plastic inspection chamber for shallow drainage.

FLEXIBLE COUPLING

▲ Exploded view of a traditional brick manhole.

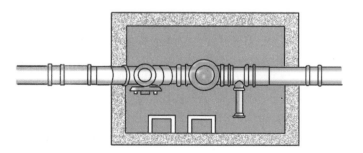

◀ Internal back-drop manhole of concrete sections, shown here in plan view and cross-section (centre left).

Porosity testing

1. Dig trial pits, to the same depth of the tanks outlet pipe where the irrigation field will be installed.
2. In the bottom of the pit, dig a smaller hole – 300 mm x 300 mm x 300 mm in size – and fill it with water.
3. Let the water drain away overnight and refill the hole in the morning. This time, record the time it takes (in seconds) for the water level to drop from being 75 per cent full to 25 per cent full. As this equates to a drop of 150 mm in the water level, it is easier if you can mark the side of your hole in advance of filling it.
4. By dividing the time by 150 you have the porosity value of the soil. This is known as the Vp. For this figure to be reasonably accurate and reliable, you should carry out a few tests in different trial holes around the irrigation area.
5. In the case of septic tank drainage, you do not actually want the drainage to work too quickly. A Vp figure of between 12 and 100 is essential for effective treatment. Outside of these figures and you may need to look at another stage for the drainage treatment, perhaps a final soakaway pit.

tank. I say small, but when you see it, or indeed the excavated hole in the ground that it will need to live in, you might not agree. With septic tanks there is a minimum size based on a 28-day storage ability, and the smallest tanks hold 1800 litres. When you consider that 2800 litres (600 gallons) is normal capacity for a family home, you can see that the annexe could easily be half the size. You should add 180 litres of capacity for every additional person living in the annexe. As a thousand litres equates to a cubic metre in volume, you can see how the size and the cost relate.

It is important that the incoming effluent does not arrive at high speed in the tank, following a steep gradient in the pipes. A biological process takes place inside the tank that relies on the contents not being disturbed too much. If you have to, make the first part of the system steeper than normal or install a backdrop manhole so you can level out the last 12 m before the tank to a gentle 1:50 to 1:70 fall in PVC-u pipework.

Septic tanks are much cheaper to buy than sealed cesspool, but more expensive to install. The reason is that they only store 'solid waste' and allow the liquid run-off to disperse into the ground through a system of perforated irrigation pipes. This-run off can end up looking like a herringbone pattern as the extent of it depends heavily on the porosity of the ground and its ability to let the water drain away. As with rainwater soakaways, the nature of the subsoil is critical to the design of the drainage irrigation system. In clay or other heavy soils, the percolation rate can be poor and a large system of perforated pipes may be needed, laid out across a big area, to compensate.

The only true way to establish the porosity is to dig a small hole and conduct a porosity test. Follow the procedure below.

Irrigation pipework has to be laid to a shallow fall if it is to work correctly; a gradient of 1:200 is ideal. Granular bed and surround of the pipes is essential, with at least 50 mm of cover over the crown of the pipe. It helps enormously to cover the pipes with a geo-textile membrane before backfilling over, keeping the soil from washing through and clogging them up. Crushed or rounded stone up to 50 mm in diameter with large voids is ideal backfill material, topped with soil.

Obviously this water is not entirely pure, and for this reason septic tanks are prohibited in sensitive areas such as aquifer zones where water is collected for supply. The Environment Agency will be able to advise you if a septic tank is acceptable in your location or whether a sealed cesspool will be necessary.

Location of septic tanks

Any drainage tank needs emptying – possibly up to once a month, but periodically in any case – so siting the tank in a position where the emptying vehicle can get at it is important. It may be possible to link hoses together to lengthen this distance and overcome other obstacles, but effluent is being pumped out here and you really do not want there to be any difficulties. A location of 30 m from the driveway or the highway is as far away as you expect to position your tank and have it emptied. At the same time, a corner of your plot that fits in with the fall of the land and is at least 7 m away from your annexe and home is ideal.

Already, many home owners engaged in extending are making provisions for those extensions to be hived off when the need arises. With house prices accelerating away from the reach of first-time buyers, the increase in annexe building can only accelerate, too, as children stay at home longer and grandparents return.

CHAPTER 6

As useful as annexes are for extending family life, to get that first step on the property ladder, you need something more and something with a value all of its own. More than just extra space, a home that can be let or sold on is only possible when planning permission is granted to divide homes. The smallest self-contained spaces are apartments, and this is where most of the housing demand now lies. Local authorities have varying policies when it comes to dividing homes into separate dwellings, and the first of those policies looks at the size of the building to begin with and asks one very important question: is it big enough to divide?

What passes as the minimum varies from one authority to the next, but as a guideline the building you are dividing needs to have at least 100 m² of floor space and often more, with at least four or five bedrooms at present. Your local planning authority's guidelines may be published on its website and in policy notes available from its offices. These will allow you to assess whether the home you are thinking of dividing is large enough to convert. I have known people extend, or convert lofts and basements in advance to enlarge the property to meet the criteria, but remember that the self-contained apartment within, will also have to meet minimum floor area requirements depending upon how many bedrooms it has to offer.

Layout

Getting the layout right is not that easy. It takes time, and you will need to consider many different factors, not least of all those fire and sound issues covered in chapter 3, but also function and drainage. At the end of the day, for any home there is an optimum layout that meets all the requirements and works well for the occupants – it is just a matter of finding it. If you are dividing a home for sale or rent, one single factor sets the design process going and fixes the objectives – the market. If the property is in an area populated by students, studio flats may be in high demand. In a business district, high-end loft-style apartments may prevail. Getting the design to fit the market in your location is the first hurdle to jump.

Three-bedroom apartments are rare, and the general opinion is that they are unwanted. The general thinking follows the line of why a family would want to rent or buy a three-bedroom apartment with no garden if they could have a three-bedroom family house with a garden instead. Families tend not to buy apartments. Single people and couples buy apartments. If you find yourself owning a three-bedroom flat, the chances are your tenant will be subletting the spare rooms to pay for his or her own rent.

Most apartment developments today contain a mix of studio, one- and two-bedroom units, with the emphasis on studio or one-bed, dependent on the local market. The top flat, I am reliably told by landlords, is always the hardest to let. The fact that it has all the stairs makes it the last one to go on most property developments. Apartments on the ground or basement floors with their own entrances are the most desirable. The top ones, those where you pass by a number of other front doors on the way to reach them, are the slowest to occupy. While it may be further to climb to get to your front door and further to go to take yourself and the refuse out, top floor apartments do have other features that are desirable. Not least of these is the fact that nobody lives on the floor above, making them much quieter. They can also have views that others do not, but generally speaking you have to work harder to let or sell them. That means that a good specification, high standard of finish and maximizing space in the roof, if need be, will all help.

Layout and fire safety

The act of dividing up a building into separate homes is known in fire engineering terms as compartmentation. Compartmentation has a good effect on fire safety because it means that fires in divided buildings seldom spread from one apartment to another – it simply hardly ever happens. Instead the risk to occupants in apartments comes from not being able to get out of them because their options for leaving are limited. Usually, there is only one way out – one hallway, one staircase, one front door, and all three

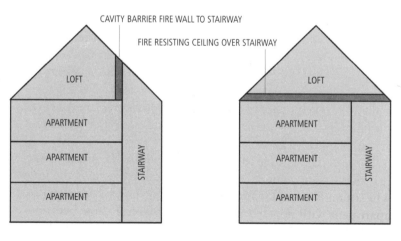

◀ The compartmentation process of fire-resisting floors and stairway walls/ceiling reduces the spread of fire inside the building.

of them are in common use. That is to say, the residents and visitors of more than one dwelling use them. If you cannot use the sole escape route, you have to stay put and wait for rescue, something people are not inclined to want to do when they know there is a fire in the building. Which is why, in home divisions that rely on single escape routes, those routes have to be protected and preserved for use as fire escapes.

The two-door approach is the essential ingredient that keeps smoke from contaminating the common spaces outside apartments – the escape route. Two doors between the rooms themselves and the outside hall or stair, one with a smoke seal fitted to the apartment's fire-resisting entrance door frame, should mean that a fire in any apartment stays in that apartment, at least for 30 minutes. That 30 minutes should be time enough for everyone to leave and the fire service to arrive. Statistically, when people die or are injured in apartment fires, it is because they were in the apartment where the fire originated, and often asleep.

There are too many cases of occupants asleep in their flats unaware that they had forgotten to switch off the deep-fat fryer. Or in my case dozing in the bath, when the aromatherapy oil burner suddenly flares up and ignites the curtains. It happens. But with some built-in fire safety measures, it can happen without anyone getting injured or embarrassed.

The internal design of any apartment needs to ensure that, if a fire breaks out inside, the occupants will not be trapped by it. Escaping from a fire is not just about options; it is about putting the risks out of the way and, for this reason, kitchens should always be located furthest from the front door and away from the bedrooms. This becomes critical when the floor level is over 4.5 m from the ground level and escape via another route, such as the windows, is not an option.

There is a limit on the size of any apartment, but it is enhanced dramatically by having a protected inner lobby. With an enclosing hall and fire doors to each of the rooms (excluding the bathroom) leading off of it, the length of the lobby itself can be anything up to 9 m from the apartment entrance. Without those fire doors, the 9-m maximum must be measured to the furthest travelling point of any of the rooms, and that will reduce the size of the apartment considerably, preventing anything other than a small one-bedroom place being created.

Plumbing to drains

Getting your drainage layout planned is one of those things that should be near the top of your list. Leaving it to last can mean

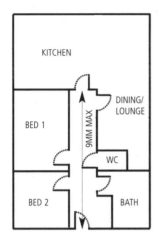

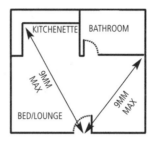

◄ Typical studio layout.

▲ Typical 2-bed apartment layout with kitchen/dining/lounge.

◄ Typical one-bed apartment layout.

leaving it to the impossible. Drainage has limitations – maximum length of pipe, minimum gradients, fixed invert levels for the existing system that you will connect from and fixed locations to which it can only be connected.

Knowing the fixed points and the limitations early on and planning your new drainage system around them is something that needs to happen right from the start. It will undoubtedly have an effect on the room layout – it may decide where the kitchens and the bathrooms will be located. Every once in a while I meet somebody who has done it the other way around and tried to bring the existing system to the new fittings, only to find that they cannot. Often, the kitchen sink has been sited on the wrong side of the building, remote from any drainage, and is made useless by the fact that a 32-mm sink waste pipe can run for only 1.7 m. Even a 50-mm waste pipe will stretch only to 4 m. (See page 239.) Inside of those runs, waste pipes cannot run across floor structures, only between the joists, because it is not structurally acceptable to bore large (anything over 25 mm in diameter) holes through a beam like a timber joist.

People are prone to doing desperate things with plumbing once they realize that they have installed a bathroom or a kitchen in a room where they cannot reach the drains. I have seen floor joists cut to house a 100-mm toilet branch waste pipe and a great deal of structural repair was necessary after it had been removed and rerouted above the floor. On another occasion, the kitchen (at the back of the property) floor in a new house was situated below the drainage in the road out the front and, with no way of making the wastewater run uphill outside of an expensive pump, the builders had left the drain to vanish beneath the back garden.

Working out a plumbing layout on two-dimensional plans is not easy; you do need to think in three dimensions. It is easy to draw a dotted line on paper, but not so easy to fix the pipe along it. Plumbing can be clipped to walls, but it cannot cross doorways and it is not pretty to look at. Boxing it in is always worth doing, as long as you maintain access to bends in the pipe where blockages might occur. I say 'might', but in truth it is only a matter of time, and showers wastes do not wait long.

Shower waste pipes not only need an absence of bends, but also need good access. The traps are usually removable to lift out the shampoo-matted hair, but still the pipes need cleaning periodically. Kitchen and dishwasher wastes are the same because of food particles and fat – another good reason, apart from the sound environmental one, that you should not be tipping coffee grounds, tea leaves, cooking oil or any other food waste down the kitchen sink.

▸ Shower-floor gulley for wet rooms.

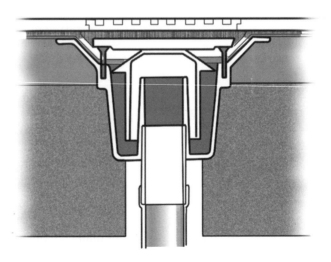

Rather than run pipes through the floor, only to cover them with expensive floor finishings that you cannot take up, raise the shower tray onto a plinth and clip the pipe to the wall above floor level. The plinth can be formed using three 75 x 50 mm bearers across the joists and decking them over with 18-mm plywood on which to seat the shower tray – the resin stone ones will want to be bedded in on dry mortar simply because they are roughly finished beneath.

The pipes can be boxed in simply or you could make a feature of the boxing itself. I have used mine to house the radiator flow and return pipes, and recess a skirting-level brick light. You could raise the boxing high enough to make a shelf out of it or form recesses for ornament displays. The point is to turn something functional into a feature – just remember to leave removable panels for access.

Shower pipes are the hardest things of all to connect simply because the pipe runs out of the tray at such a low level, practically floor level. Floor level is always a bad place to start, and shower pipes almost always have to run between floor joists unless the tray is raised and you step up into the shower. Both of my showers have the latter arrangement. It was only way in which they could be plumbed in where they had to go. Steps are not desirable, but if you keep them to a maximum of 100 mm they are not much of a hindrance for the able-bodied.

Wet rooms

Wet shower rooms are another matter entirely. As popular as they are, you are asking for problems installing one in an upper-floor apartment. One of the most common disputes in blocks of apartments is over water leaks – where they spring from and who is responsible for them. For wet shower rooms, you require the floor of the room itself to act as the shower tray, and for that it must be perfectly sealed against water and laid to fall towards a gulley waste set level within the floor finish. In this case, however, they must of course be built into the floor structure rather than above it.

These gullies are specially designed for this location and are larger than conventional shower wastes. Still, they take running water in much the same way, and are removable for cleaning out. They have a larger diameter than a conventional trap, but the outlet drops out at an angle to take a 40-mm diameter pipe just the same. The inner part can be removed for cleaning by simply unscrewing it from the outer housing. In the past, they may have been quite robust aluminium or steel fittings, but now that the

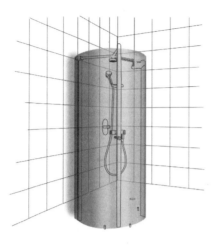

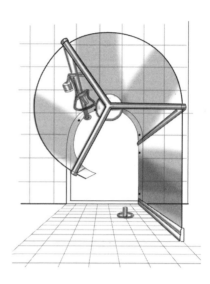

▲ Even in wet rooms, shower screens are necessary when other appliances (basin, WC etc.) are fitted in the same space.

market has grown they are mass-produced in plastic the same as everything else and seem to be perfectly functional.

If wet shower rooms have a problem, it is with the pipe levels. Enough of a difference in level must exist between the wet floor at which the grating of the shower will be set flush, and the invert of the drains into which it will connect. This difference will largely be occupied by the gulley itself, but also by the pipework, which must run to a suitable gradient if the wastewater is to run away into the drains.

Wet shower rooms tend to be compatible with both tiled floors and sheet flooring. You might not have heard of the latter, but sheet flooring is becoming increasingly popular. It was once the domain of care homes, where wet room showers for wheelchair

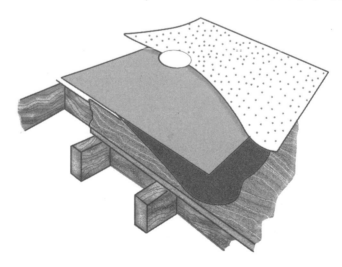

▸ Welded sheet flooring over plywood-decked timber floor.

users and elderly residents are commonplace. Sheet flooring is solvent-welded (glued) down to the floor screed in one piece and dressed up the walls where skirting would be in any other room. It is textured for a non-slip finish, comes in a range of colours and has the guaranteed water resistance that tiling lacks. It is perfectly suited to solid ground floors where it can be laid over a new screeded wet room having had the cement and sand screed towelled to fall towards the gulley. The only mistake here is to rush into it on a still damp floor and be faced with trying to get it up when the bubbles appear.

Timber-floor wet rooms
For timber floors, you can try to achieve the same by bonding a marine-grade plywood over the floor finish before welding down the sheet flooring. To achieve the falls, the plywood decking will need to be glued and screwed down over firring pieces. These are cut fillets of timber shaped to a five-degree fall, and you will need to space them no more than 600 mm apart for 18-mm thick plywood. Any further or any thinner with the ply will amount to movement in the floor, and it must be rock solid.

A hybrid of the two systems is available – a cross between a wet room and a conventional shower tray – but it is prone to leak when it is not perfect. A recessed shower tray is a conventional tray hidden beneath a raised floor. The floor surrounding it is dressed with tanking boards (waterproof boarding) that are lined to create the wet floor. My problem with these systems is that they are intended to be installed on timber suspended floors. Indeed, they rely upon the gaps between the joists for the shower trap to settle into. If I explain step by step how they seem to work you can make your own decision as to whether to run with it.

The system relies on the existing boarding being clean, fixed down soundly with plenty of screws and also level. Depending on the age of the property, this in itself is likely to be a stumbling block. Not many floors are clean, level and well fixed. Assuming yours are, you would first brush-apply a liquid primer to the floorboards and up the wall where the skirting boards were before you removed them. If you are not sure about your floorboards' integrity, covering them with WPB (waterproof bonded) plywood is worth doing anyway. Glue and screw the sheets down to the existing boards. This should help you to achieve a stable floor free of movement, which is essential. The proprietary tanking boards are then laid over this subfloor, bedded in a flexible tile adhesive. There are many tile adhesives now which can be used in timber floor situations and will remain flexible, but I still recommend

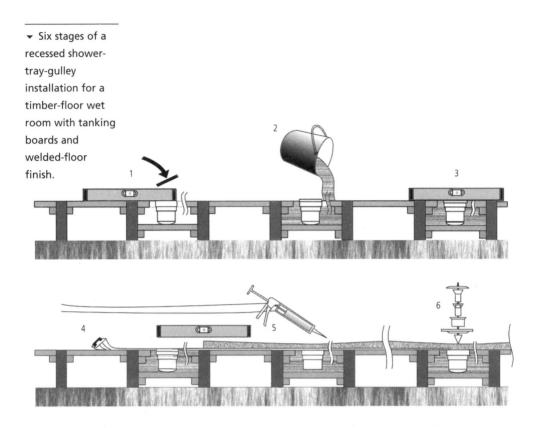

▼ Six stages of a recessed shower-tray-gulley installation for a timber-floor wet room with tanking boards and welded-floor finish.

adding a little of the flexible additive with which you can treat ordinary tile adhesive. You need a product that will bond but not set brittle, one that. like decorators' caulking, will give a little without cracking. The adhesive is combed out in the usual tiling fashion, then the boards laid, working from the centre of the room out to the walls. This floating tanking floor is then, the following day, taped up at the joints with 'tanking tape'. Internal and external corner angles are fitted and the tile finishings laid.

The shower trap needs to be fully supported in position between the joists, and this is usually done by sitting it into a plywood box that is mortar-filled around it for stability. The box sides are fixed to the sides of the joists (stage 2 in diagram above).

Studio flats

Studio flats are by their very nature small – the size of a hotel room in many cases – but, with a lot of thought, you can still fit a lotl into a very small space. You just have to think in three dimensions.

I learned this fact in a hotel in Copenhagen where, as a family of four, we stayed for a few days. With virtually no floor area and all three beds stacked up past a large opening window like shelves on the wall reached via a fixed ladder, getting into bed at night had to be carefully choreographed. This was extreme space-saving for the passing traveller, and not many of us would want to hang ourselves up like a bat every night, but it did make me realize what is possible given limitations on floor area.

Instead of sleeping shelves or pull-down beds, sleeping galleries are a common feature in high-ceiling studio flats. These, the smallest of apartments, are often tenanted by students and singles who will spend little time beyond sleeping here. For them, a compact layout is not a problem. I inspected some recently that had alternate-tread staircases to the gallery leading up from the lounge/dining/kitchenette. The only other enclosed space was the shower room (shower rooms take up less space than bathrooms), separated by partitioning, but formed beneath the gallery. The kitchenette was open plan to the lounge because a wall here would merely have robbed even more space without reason. The floor space was actually only 18 m² not including the sleeping gallery, which was a little cramped for headroom at 1.9 m to the ceiling, but performing a valuable function by design.

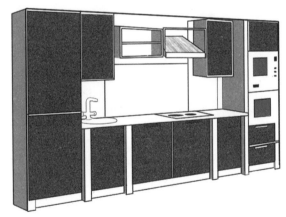

▾ Built-in kitchenette.

There is an acceptable maximum size for a studio flat, and it is prescribed by fire safety requirements. For a typical flat with one entrance door for entry and escape, 9 m should be the furthest distance across the living-area floor. That means you can add extra for worktops at the kitchenette end and for the bathroom. Few studio flats have a problem with this limit.

Sleeping galleries

Studio flats often are tight for bedroom space, and one popular way to overcome this problem is to create a mezzanine floor, or a raised sleeping deck area that is open plan with the living space below and not contained within a separate room – a sleeping gallery. Like the galleries in theatres and other public buildings, these elevated platforms have protection from falling provided along the edge by balustrading that overlooks the space below.

I have spent only the occasional night in a sleeping gallery and always in hotel rooms, but they work extremely well when you

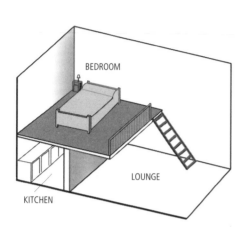

BEDROOM

LOUNGE

KITCHEN

▲ Sleeping-gallery floor, shown shaded.

have a floor-space limitation, but plenty of ceiling height. In many ways, you might think of them as an extended version of the cabin and high-sleeper beds that are so popular for children. Instead of having a metre or so of headroom underneath for a desk, the sleeping gallery can have as much headroom as the flat can afford. Galleries that extend into the roof space are ideal, as they do not tend to rob the space below or above them in this respect.

There are four simple rules for sleeping galleries, which when all is said are done are additional floors, albeit small and open-plan ones.

1. The stairs that serve the gallery must descend to within 3 m of the flat entrance door so that escape is easily reached.
2. At least 50 per cent of the flat's floor area must be visible from the gallery, so that you can see a problem below and have early warning of any need to escape.
3. The gallery must be sized so that no part of the floor area is further than 7.5 m from the top of the staircase leading down.
4. The kitchen part of the studio flat where a gallery exists must either be enclosed in fire-resisting construction and not open-plan, or be sufficiently remote from the gallery stairs to ensure that a fire in the kitchen area will not cut off the escape route.

The above criteria do not apply when the gallery has an egress window (meaning the window is within 4.5 m of ground level outside and is adequately sized) or if it is served by two sets of stairs leading to separate escape routes.

The staircase problem
It may not be possible to fit in a traditional staircase to serve the gallery; a normal straight flight of 13 risers and 12 treads occupies at least 3.5 m of space over both floors when you include the landings. You can squash that down with tapered treads (a.k.a. winders) that turn the direction of the stair as it climbs. Three winders at the bottom and three at the top can reduce the length dramatically. When space is really tight, however, you may have to resort to a narrow spiral staircase or even an alternate-tread staircase. Spiral stairs never seem to save much room and cannot help but become something of a feature

themselves in a small home. Tapered treads are those that overlap each other, paddle-shaped, as they climb, reducing the length of the staircase on plan. In some ways they are more tricky to use than ladders – at least with them you know you have to hang on. With alternate treads being a stairs-ladder hybrid, the basic process of moving between floors becomes an ergonomic challenge. You have to set off on the right foot, retain your balance, hang on to the handrails (two are needed) and, above all else, never change your mind on the way down. To do so can either result in you becoming stranded mid stair, waiting for help to arrive, or completing the journey, rear end over breast.

Sleeping galleries have to be small. If they are not, they evolve into upper floors and, worse than that, open-plan upper floors. If that happens, they are likely to need two staircases, each providing an alternative escape down into a separate part of the apartment below. It would not help having both staircases descending into the same room, albeit a different corner of the same room. For them to be viable as escape routes, they must provide the occupier with the opportunity of getting out by another route when one set of stairs becomes blocked due to a fire below. Ideally, one staircase should descend into the protected lobby of the apartment. To do this, a fire door will be needed to separate the gallery from the stair. I have seen some apartments designed in this way, and it works quite well.

The bedrooms would extend out on a gallery floor over the lounge with dining areas below, to perhaps three-quarters of their width. A glass or conventional balustrade can then be run along the edge. Instead of the stairs leading up from the lounge, they rise from the apartment's entrance lobby to a landing and a door to the bedroom. You might be thinking, what is the point of having an open-plan layout like a sleeping gallery if you have to get on and off it via an enclosed stairway. Fire safety is the point. The enclosed stairway provides recumbent occupants with a sanctuary to escape to and a way out of the apartment if the smoke alarms wake them.

Basement flats

Basements flats need a separate door for escape away from the main entrance door, which begs a good question. In late Victorian homes, the basement was often just a coal cellar accessed from inside and entirely below ground. If this is the case with your home and its cellar, then you will have a problem converting it to a separate flat and would be better off adapting it as kitchen or bathroom for the lower floor of a maisonette. The alternative escape in such an arrangement can only be a separate staircase leading from a separate part of the basement, up to a different part of the building above. In other words, a fully subterranean basement cannot be divided off as a separate apartment unless it is quite large and stretched out, with a staircase at either end. In the late Victorian home, the cellar was purely a coal store and seldom large enough to achieve this.

As it happens, some basements are only partly below ground, and those with their own external entrances are common, particularly in early Victorian homes. These are almost Georgian in style, and you have to descend steps at the front or rear of the building to get down to the door to what would have been the kitchen and servants' quarters. The fact that you can arrive and leave from it independently is an essential feature when dividing off a basement to form an apartment in its own right.

With the an external front entrance to the basement flat, you can usually agree on suitable escape windows to provide the other, emergency exit route out the back. Those windows will, of course, need to fit the criteria for escape out on to ground level, but they will do instead of a door if you can get out and away. It does mean that the ground level outside of them cannot be more than about a metre above the basement floor without having to raise a deck up to the windowsill. Escape windows cannot be higher than about 1.1 m above floor level and, in the past, developers have at times had to build up a platform to get a leg-up, as it were.

Sometimes basement light wells are all the space that exists outside of windows, and these will not prove so easy to overcome. There is little point in climbing out of a window into a narrow shaft if you cannot get out of it to the ground above.

Damp and damp-proofing

Basements on older properties are not likely to be damp-proofed to the standard expected today. Invariably they suffer with dampness, poor insulation and poor daylight levels, and to bring them into use as a self-contained flat or part of a maisonette will mean resolving all of these issues. Damp-proofing needs to be tailored to the level of dampness present or expected. There are systems for internal damp-proofing that will not resist active water pressure exuding from the walls and floor, and others that will. Needless to say, there is a good deal of difference between them in the cost.

At the extreme end of damp-proofing, rigid plastic sheeting that has a profiled face to create a drainage void is secured to the walls using sealed fixings such as an advanced plug-and-screw

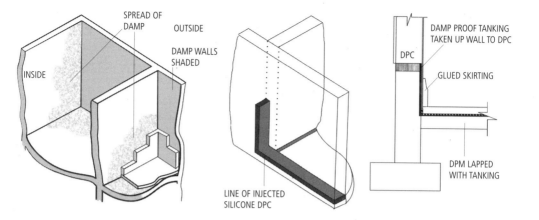

SPREAD OF DAMP
OUTSIDE
DAMP WALLS SHADED
INSIDE

LINE OF INJECTED SILICONE DPC

DAMP PROOF TANKING TAKEN UP WALL TO DPC
DPC
GLUED SKIRTING
DPM LAPPED WITH TANKING

arrangement. This form of tanking fails only if the right fixings are not used or the workmanship was poor. It does need some attention to detail and can be a pain to fit around corners and against door jambs, but it is effective. The end result will divert the active pressure of water from flooding or rising damp away from the inner linings and finishings of the apartment. The masonry wall and concrete floor behind, however, will still be saturated. If they are not to suffer in the long term, the water will need to be drained out. For most systems, that means collecting it in a sump and installing a submersible pump with a float switch. When the sump fills with the drained water, the pump kicks in and empties it via pipework leading to the drainage system.

For damp-proofing against dampness rather than actual groundwater, a liquid or rubberized sheet membrane is likely to be sufficient. The unfortunate thing about these products is that they have to be applied to a dry wall, making them more suited to the new-build market than conversions. The brush-on solutions can be based on bitumen, rubber latex or polyurethane resin, and remain flexible when set. Most have to be applied in more than one coat.

For any tanking to be successful, in addition to treating the external walls and concrete floors, you should also treat internal walls. Quite often they will not have a damp-proof course or they will be in contact with the external walls and drawing damp from them. The tanking needs to climb all the walls to at least 150 mm above ground level. If you have access to the ground around the outside of the building, installing a surface-water drain will help remarkably, although it will mean digging down alongside the basement walls to install it. The trench can then be drained by a surface-water drainage pipe with holes in the top to collect groundwater and divert it to a soakaway away from the

▲ Internal walls and floors can also be damp next to basement external walls.

basement. The trench is backfilled with pebble-sized stones, rather than earth, to keep it free-draining, and a polythene damp-proof membrane can be pinned against the basement wall to give added protection.

Apartments, whether below ground or not, need adequate protection from damp, and damp can arrive in one or more of three ways: rising damp, penetrating damp and damp air.

Rising damp

The rarest of all forms of damp rises from the ground when a damp-proof course and membrane do not exist or have become damaged. We started building damp-proof courses into our new homes in 1870, but there is no guarantee that a property built after that year will have one, or indeed that it will be an effective one. Slate was used for many years, before bitumen, then polythene, but the quality of Victorian and Edwardian homes varied from builder to builder.

I have seen more rising damp caused by bridging the damp-proof course than anything else. As years go by, properties see garden levels raised and pathways, patios and driveways laid with no regard for the wall's damp-proof course, which was likely to have been only a brick above the original ground level. Once water gets across above the damp-proof course and into a porous structure such as a brick wall, it rises naturally – creating a permanent damp zone to the walls above the inside floor level.

Electrical moisture meters that take in depth readings (rather than surface readings) can help to determine the presence of rising damp. These meters have sharp metal probes that can be pushed through the plaster finish to take readings. Failing that, holes are pre-drilled to enable longer prongs of up to 250 mm to take deeper readings from the centre of the masonry wall. This is important because surface damp looks and smells the same whatever the cause, and more often than not the cause is one of the other two forms of damp and not rising damp at all.

Penetrating damp

You could argue that rising damp is a form of penetrating damp, but the cause is what is important, not the label. Damp-proofing specialists do not always trouble themselves with finding the cause, so busy are they with selling you the cure. With any form of damp, there is always a cause. A leaking gutter or damaged roof, a bridged cavity wall, a vertical damp-proof course cut away when a PVC-u replacement window was fitted – the list is endless. I know of one recent damp problem caused simply by the occupant innocently drilling a hole through the wall (and the cavity tray damp-proof course within it) and feeding an electrical cable through to his garden. A small hole, I grant you, but one that allowed water to track through on the cable and be absorbed into the inner wall and its plaster finish.

When the wind is behind rain and driving at a wall under pressure, it can find its way in through any holes or indeed through the wall itself if is a single leaf of brick. So, if you must, you can think of penetrating damp as rising damp that comes sideways from above ground, rather than up from below.

Damp air

As long as the temperature is less than 24°C, and the moisture in the air represents more than 18.75 g per thousand, condensation occurs. Condensation occurs in most homes, but it is in those where it is not acknowledged and dispersed that it becomes a problem. In the winter, when the warm moist air we generate inside our homes by simply breathing, cooking and washing collides with the colder surfaces of the walls and roof, condensation appears on the surface. You will know how it appears frequently on the surface of a single glass pane, but less frequently on double-glazing. Insulation has a big role to play in keeping the level of condensation down, but ventilation is also essential. Homes will sweat if they are sealed up because that moisture cannot escape, and so breathable materials must also be used with insulating materials if it is to work.

As well as surface condensation, which tends to result in black mould growing in the corners of rooms and behind kitchen appliances such as washing machines, interstitial condensation can occur inside the wall or roof itself.

When the climate changes from cooler to warmer, condensation evaporates away and the structure dries out, but continual soaking with condensation can degrade things such as insulation and metal fixings over time. Interstitial condensation, though, can easily be controlled. A vapour barrier (such as aluminium foil or thin polythene) can prevent it reaching through to the inside surface, and this barrier needs to be behind the finishings. Foil-backed plasterboards have it prefixed to the back of the boards, so using them guarantees its presence. Polyurethane insulation boards and thin insulation products have foil layers, too. Used within the inner surfaces of walls and roofs, they do an excellent job in resisting moisture-laden air entering the structure, helping to keep it dry. Of all the materials available in vapour checks, aluminium foil is said to be the most effective.

Our normal interior linings of plasterboard and emulsion paint are extremely permeable and offer little, if any, resistance to vapour. It is therefore not a good idea to insulate a timber frame wall without a vapour barrier on the inside face, as it will become soaked with condensing vapour at some point in the middle. In dividing off your apartment and lining it with internal insulation products, you will help to ensure a dry as well as a warm environment. I have yet to see condensation on the surfaces of walls that have been internally insulated because they are warm to the touch.

Rising damp is something entirely different. It comes from the ground up through the foundations and into the wall structure, and as a result ground salts are often discovered in the dampness. To discover their presence involves taking samples or readings from inside the wall and not on the surface of it. This means having to damage the finishings, but if insulation upgrading is going to be done this should not matter. A sample of the mortar from within the wall can then be taken for laboratory analysis. It requires analysis because hygroscopic salts are present in building materials anyway, although they are more obvious in the case of new buildings where time and the rain have yet to wash them out. For rising damp to be diagnosed, the salts found from within the mortar of a brick wall must contain nitrates and chlorides that are found in groundwater – proof that the damp is rising up from the ground.

Measuring damp is often done using electronic resistance or capacitance meters equipped with a pair of penetrating needle like prongs that are meant to be able penetrate the wall and detect rising damp, assuming you can get them through the plaster. The prongs are questionably short and you cannot get them through to the brickwork without drilling holes first, but then I have never been that confident about the readings they give. I do not think it wise to base a rising-damp diagnosis on meter readings alone.

As hygroscopic salts will have invaded the damp plaster, the plaster will have been damaged and must be removed. After any internal plaster is hacked off to at least 300 mm above the surface of the damp, a series of holes is drilled into the wall. Only one side of a wall that is anything up to 450 mm thick need be drilled out, and that is usually the inside. A low-pressure system that allows the liquid time to disperse more convincingly into the brickwork is used, and the solvent-based fluid that is injected usually has a siliconate or stearate ingredient that repels water. It smells something awful (as do all organic solvents, which are high in volatile organic compounds), and this is not work to be done in an occupied home – it needs to be well ventilated and vacant.

On-site checks when treating rising damp
◆ Check that the holes are not spaced more than 175 mm apart.
◆ Check that the holes are at least 50 mm deep.
◆ Check that position of the holes is at least 150mm above outside ground level
◆ Watch to see if the solution exudes back out of the brickwork before the injection is stopped, proof that it has saturated in.

It can take a long time for brickwork to dry out – a rate of around 25 mm per month is often quoted, but it depends on the temperature and humidity of the surrounding air. Either way, it can take a 215-mm thick solid wall nine months to dry out fully after treatment, but nobody waits that long before they replaster a treated wall.

Replastering is done with a renovating mix that contains cement rather than gypsum; however, if you are internally lining the wall with insulation and plasterboard, this is likely to be a far better solution than any wet plaster. Stainless-steel fixings to treated battens that are secured to the wall over a polythene damp-proof course is the ideal way to dry-line a previously damp wall. Keep the plasterboard off the floor at the bottom; the skirting will cover the gap.

Developers in a hurry to divide old homes into apartments often pay scant attention to damp-proofing, not giving it the time it deserves, but damp does not go away by itself and it is much more expensive to deal with after the work is complete and the property is occupied. If damp-proofing is necessary, make sure that it is one of the first things you do.

Solving problems by design

The stacking principle

Wherever possible, apartments that are divided horizontally work best when similar rooms are stacked above and below each other – bedrooms over bedrooms, kitchens over kitchens, bathroom over bathrooms, etc. Adhering to this principle reduces noise disturbances and makes installing plumbing, services and drainage a lot easier. Vertical stack pipes and service shafts can rise up and bring everything to the same point in each apartment, reducing the length of waste pipes and the number of connections. Quite apart from the physical limits of plumbing, having an outside wall crawling with pipework is not pretty. It is not unusual to see the rear walls of divided homes alive with pipework on three- and four-storey conversions. Impossibly long runs of pipes snake across walls collecting other pipes along the way, via hopper heads and branches. Some plumbing systems have evolved over the years as the property has added appliances (such as en-suite bathroom showers, dishwashers and washing machines), resulting in an uncontrolled growth that rivals a spider's web. Internal soil vent pipes inside service shafts that raise electricity, water, telephone and gas in one tidy and protected duct are the way to go.

Sizing rooms

You might think any size of room is acceptable today, given the space limits imposed on housing, but there are recognized minimum limits still in use to avoid people mistaking the airing cupboard for their bedroom. The smallest bedrooms (second bedrooms) are acceptable if they are at least 4.7 m^2 in floor area. That is about 7 ft x 7 ft in imperial (carpet-style) measurements. Although this is the minimum for a single bedroom, often design standards imposed by local councils look for the main double bedroom to be more than twice this size, at 10 m^2. Kitchens can be smaller, falling in at 7 m^2, but quite often it makes more sense to design kitchenettes that are incorporated into the living area of apartments without those living areas needing to be much bigger. A kitchen/dining/living room as a single open-plan space is achievable in a floor area of 15 m^2. Bathrooms may be dominated by the sanitaryware, but it is important to leave a small amount of clear floor space – at least a square metre to stand on and to safely allow you to move between and use the room.

It is critical to set out the appliances correctly to make them accessible. So many bathrooms have the toilet or the bath in the wrong place, and you have to be a contortionist to employ them, or move between them and the basin.

Light and air

Habitable rooms, with the exception of bathrooms and kitchens, need daylight and windows that are openable to provide ventilation. The window's glazed area should equal at least 10 per cent of the floor area of the room it serves for providing daylight, but only 5 per cent needs to be openable (to provide one-twentieth of the floor area) in ventilation area.

Theoretically, you might be able to rely on mechanical fans to pull air in and out to bedrooms and living rooms bereft of windows, but who in their right mind would. Apart from the power drain on your electricity supply, the noise and sheer misery of having a powered fan whining away all to three air changes an hour would make it more of a vessel than a home. There is, however, another and much better solution for internal rooms, to be found in whole building ventilation systems. These can be served by passive ductwork stacks that draw the air up through the whole building to the roof space, where it is drawn out through a vent and replaced with a fresh supply of air ducted in. This is not air conditioning, but is air handling all the same and much less unpleasant to live with than extractor fans, particularly as the warm air can pass through a heat exchanger and be used to warm the fresh filtered air replacing it.

These systems are great for removing pollens and other pollutants, and improve air quality in a small home very efficiently. They do, however, have to be incorporated into the design at an early stage and will add to the size of the service shafts passing through the building.

Kitchens

Whether your kitchen space is a room in itself or part of another, you may have to match up to some minimum standards imposed by your local authority housing department. In enforcing the Housing Act, and encouraging minimum standards of housing in its district, it will have some ideas about what facilities are acceptable, and kitchens are usually included. Some facilities that may be required to meet the standards are listed below:

Worktop space
Work surfaces should usually be at least 500 mm deep, and the least you could reasonably expect is a standard kitchen unit of 1500 mm in length. A sink and drainer can occupy 1000 mm.

Cooker space
In new homes, cooker spaces are typically gaps in the worktop, 600 mm wide and 600 mm deep. They may be either gas-pointed or fitted with an electric cooker point, but note that the 30-amp ring main is not sufficient. Electric cooker points are generally 45-amp circuits and supplied with fused connection units. Cooker points fitted with hood extraction units must be in reach of, if not on, external walls because they must be terminated outside and not fitted with recirculation filters. Cooker spaces should be at least 500 mm from door openings in the same wall. As a landlord, you may choose whether to supply and fit white goods (cooker, washer/dryer, fridge freezer and dishwasher) or whether you will simply provide the space and plumbing for them. If you do choose to supply and fit as the landlord, you will be responsible for them and their safety. White goods packages are available to developers

▸ Space-saving fittings, such as carousels and door bins, are available for compact kitchen designs.

from reputable manufacturers, and you will see that new-home builders use them as standard.

Refrigerator space

As with cookers, a space of 600 mm width and 600 mm depth must be available for a refrigerator. The height does not usually come into it, so it may be a small under-worktop unit with a freezer box or a tall fridge/freezer. At least 500 mm from the side of a doorway is often preferred, and it should not be directly next to the cooker space.

Extractor fan

If the extractor fan is not a hood-type fan above the cooker, a separate fan should be located as near to the cooker as possible and be capable of drawing out 60 litres of air per second.

Washing machine space

You will need 630 mm depth by 600 mm width to accommodate a washing machine and its plumbing. The most economical use of space is to be found alongside the kitchen sink, where combined waste pipes can be used that accept the drainage hose and use the sink waste pipe to discharge to. The hot- and cold-water supply will also be close at hand for connection.

Power points

Kitchens, of course, can never have enough power points and it may be unreasonable to expect anything fewer than three or four double-socket outlets.

Food storage and utensil space

A volume of 1.5 m³ might seem like a lot in terms of cupboard space, but in fact it is often considered to be the least you can expect for food storage. Picture a larder cupboard and you have it, but it could equally amount to a double floor under unit and a wall cupboard.

Styles and materials

Kitchens can be very short-lived. They receive a great deal of use and suffer a great deal of wear and tear. Some of the materials we use today (actually most of them) are not up to this and, if they are to last for as long as a decade, they will have to be looked after more than most of us would care to look after them. In a tenanted apartment, the life expectancy of a fitted kitchen is frighteningly short at three years. It is sad to note that in some

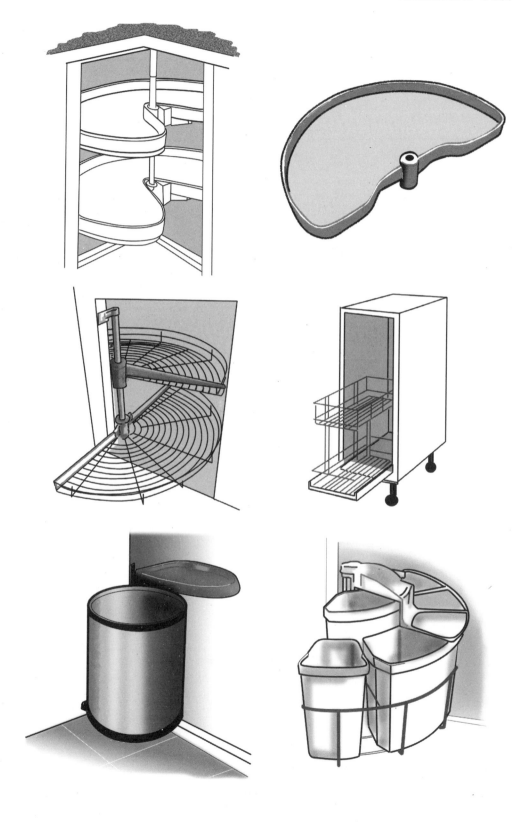

flats let through housing associations and paid by welfare benefit, kitchens have to be replaced annually.

Of course, you cannot generalize on the basis of background any more than you can hope your tenants will be cast like the Von Trapps from *the Sound of Music* and treat your property as if it were their own. You have to be realistic and prepared for the worst, and that means replacing worktops and door fronts regularly. As a landlord, budgeting for repairs and renewals is critical. My advice is to go with something that helps that – a polished white-door kitchen is easier to clean then a grained white finish or a solid wood style. Laminated worktops are cheap and cheerful, but not repairable. If you actually wanted to spend the money, the resin stone hybrids are messy to install, but highly durable. More importantly, they can be resurfaced and repaired when damaged. Fragranite is a resin with 80 per cent granite particles – these afford it strength, durability and scratch-resistance. Able to resist temperatures up to 280°C, which should just about cope with hot pans but not actual fire, like ceramic, it comes as either polished smooth or textured. Materials such as these are used as work surfaces in schools, which will give you some idea of how much abuse they can take.

In a contemporary apartments, the commercial look of stainless steel or the quality of cast glass may be the upmarket solution for the high-end market, but even here you cannot use these materials for the lettings. These are the kind of wow factor extras that you use when selling for the maximum possible price. They both look great, but repairing any damage, or even replacing them, will prove so expensive that only the owners of them will treat them better than they treat each other. White is the choice for longevity and is particularly valued when the kitchen is not blessed with a wealth of daylight.

Assuming your newly divided apartment is for a family member and personal taste is let loose in the interior design, the kitchen is the place to start from and white becomes just one option.

Interior design

Apartments are by their very nature small homes, so introducing a strong theme to the kitchen inevitably means having to run with it through the rest of the home. As luck would have it, an apartment is probably the only sort of home where you can do this convincingly and boldly. The condensed space allows you to be creative and really push the boat out on a design theme. If the kitchen is the hub of the house, the engine room, then it is even more central to the design of an apartment, and it makes sense to start the style here. You can tone it down a bit by the time you get to the bedroom.

Contemporary

Contemporary literally means of the present time, and hence it is a moveable feast. Whatever is in vogue at the present time is contemporary – on its way to becoming out of vogue and replaced by something else. Right now, contemporary design means simple with clean lines and smooth polished materials such as glass, chrome and hardwood. This comes with the added bonus of the look of quality and expense about it. Texture is used to contrast with all that smoothness in the form of woolly rugs, hairy cushions and other 'distressed' accessories.

A stone kitchen worktop would be an unnecessary extravagance in most apartment conversions, but, if the market dictates a high-end finish, granite will be one of the few choices that will be worth it. Of the natural stones, granite is the hardest wearing and perhaps most easily maintained material and would therefore suit a let property. It might just be possible to scratch it if you try hard enough, but generally the polished surface has a diamond-hard quality about it. The colour of granite varies from the charcoal blacks that are very stylish to almost pale terracotta. If you are going to order granite worktops, you are going to have to become a perfectionist when it comes to checking the installation. Make sure that the corners are seamlessly joined and are finished perfectly at the edges. Stone is exacting and, if you are paying that kind of money for it, you want it to be right and look right. One of the great advantages of having a worktop honed from a single piece of stone such as granite is that the sink bowl can also be cut from it as one homogenous lump. I've made that sound so attractive, haven't I, but these sink bowls have a natural free-form look that has to be the very best appearance money can buy.

In the kitchen, it begins with stainless steel and what started in the millennium with just the cooker's extractor hood has stretched to the worktops and cupboard doors. This material was unheard of for appliances in the domestic kitchen world not all that long ago, but it has become rapidly popular. Stainless steel was the favoured material in commercial kitchens, and to me it still looks a little sterile and harsh in an apartment.

Choose LEDs as worktop lighting to reduce the wattage and the glare that other lights will send bouncing off the surfaces, and steer clear of stainless-steel worktops in let properties. They scratch very easily and, without care, the surface will soon look like a scarred battlefield. This by the way is also a product that requires a specialist manufacture and is not conducive to cheap shortcuts.

If all that metal is a bit industrialized for you, white is just as contemporary in design. You just might need to use a bold colour to pick it out – ocean blue tiles, for example. Black might be the new white, but whenever I see it in kitchens and bedrooms it says bachelor pad to me. That might just be me, of course. Black-and-white is certainly an easy theme, furniture-wise, but you do have to careful not to turn the place into a chessboard.

Minimalist

If anything suits a small home better, let me know. The minimalist lifestyle is fiction to me. Like a lot of people I am a hoarder and, although we tend to have a good clear-out every year or two, the volume of space that I need to live in only gets bigger.

In spite of this I am committed (mentally) to becoming a minimalist as I grow older. Minimalism to me seems grounded in the perfectly sensible realization that, as you cannot take it with you, you might as well get rid of it now. It is a challenge to see how few material goods you need in life and, if we are to be brutally honest, it is not that many. This philosophy will hold you in good stead if you are going to live in an apartment. Indeed, in studio flats it is practically mandatory.

Glass is a favourite material for me, but it is worth considering only in high-end apartment developments that will be sold on. Made to order by companies that specialize in cast glass furnishings, it creates an original and functional worktop that can be backed up with a continuous one-piece splashback. Heat resistant and easy to clean, it is the only worktop material that can be lit from below. Be careful with glass, though. There is a tendency to think that it is entirely see-through and colourless – it is not. The exposed edges have a depth of greenness to them and because of that you cannot use colours in the kitchen that would clash with green. You might consider a dark stone-tiled floor and white or cream walls, or come to that a dark stone-coloured wall and white or cream floor tiles.

▾ Apartment kitchens can be compact and choosing the right design is critical.

Shaker

The Shakers were of the opinion that the kitchen should be, and appear to be, a hub of calmness and efficiency bathed in cool colours. Shaker doors are simplistic but stylish in their clean lines and square edges, free from decoration or arty bits, which under the Shaker principle only clutter the appearance. When you look at a Shaker kitchen, it should calm you. Everything should be just where you need it to be – functional. The only drawback is that in the land of starter homes this could be misinterpreted as cheap. Natural wood worktops might help to change that, but the kitchen doors will need a more colourful paint finish to a smooth eggshell or matt coating that is nothing less than perfect (in other words, factory-applied – not hand-painted).

Functional design

Having your kitchen designed for free by the installers is one way forward, and without a doubt it is worth having their advice in this area. I would not, however, rely upon it completely – you need to guide them rather than let them guide you. This will be your kitchen and giving the options plenty of thought now will pay off.

Start by measuring up the space, and prepare a scale plan of the room with all the exterior walls marked and coloured. The external walls are everything to kitchen design – daylight, ventilation, drainage, extractors, water etc. The more outside walls you have, the greater flexibility you have over where things go. Next, mark in the services that exist at present and their position – gas, water, power points. All of these can be extended, but there are limitations. If your kitchen is internal and bereft of even one outside wall, you need to avoid bringing gas in here entirely. Instead all the appliances should be electric as, with this fuel, combustion air is not required and carbon monoxide poisoning not a threat. You will still have to duct out an extractor fan and, if the room is enclosed, duct in some fresh air (purge ventilation).

With this done, you can decide on what other appliances you want and whether you have the room to fit them in. Storage space is important and, if it comes to it, reducing the size or the number of appliances to meet the storage needs could be necessary.

Many years ago when domestic engineering received government advice, the ideal arrangement of the kitchen was drawn by a triangle between the cooker, sink and fridge. The 'efficiency triangle', as it is known, is still used in advice today. Although the theory is sound, the dimension of the sides (between

3.3 and 6.6 m) is too big for most homes, let alone apartments. Ergonomics is all very well, but it turns out the perfect kitchen is circular and that kind of excludes it from being a separate room. It could, however, be adapted to the corner kitchenette position in an open-plan layout. Fitting a curved or diagonal worktop across a corner to divide off the kitchen, breakfast bar–style, could work very well.

You may realize that you do not have the space for everything you would like, which should help you focus on what your needs really are. Technology is helping all the time when it comes to space-saving solutions. Tumble dryers that condense the water vapour internally and require no external vents can be located anywhere there is a power point. Built-in refrigerators and ovens come in a variety of sizes that will fit out everything from a caravan-sized flat or an executive home.

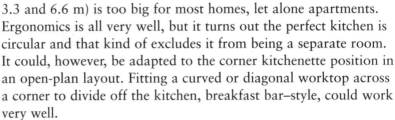

▼ Bar tops and fold-down dining tables are great space savers.

Deciding where the kitchen sink goes is a good place to start – usually because there are not that many options. Sinks need some daylight and we traditionally locate the sink under the window so that the domestic engineer can look out while doing the washing up, pondering the meaning of life. Directing artificial lighting down from the centre of the ceiling can mean you have to stand in your own shadow, so think about the relationship between the sink and lighting. I have seen apartment kitchens peppered with recessed spotlights and looking like a barn door after a shotgun blast, but still somehow failing to light the work zone. With kitchen wall units either side, you should be able to carry a light plinth over the sink that can house hidden lights. The top of the units should frame the window head so that the window is not hindered. Alternatives to creating 'light bridges' such as this come in the form of the cable lighting kits that stretch taut wires for spots to fix to and string between walls or units. They also look great in recessed kitchenettes.

Functional layouts

Not just for fire protection, entrance lobbies or hallways are vital to the successful layout of an apartment. Without them, you can

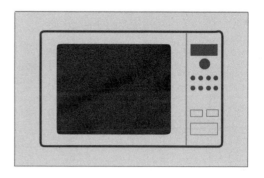

only enter one room from another, and that creates all kinds of difficulties when bedrooms and living rooms are on the same floor.

A lobby does not have to be big – indeed, it is important to limit the size of it – but it will prove invaluable all the same. The apartment will be accessed through its own 'front door' and, if this is located within a common hall or stairway, the front door will need to be fire-resisting to protect that hall or stairway. It will be an essential escape route for all the occupants of the building in a fire, and as such it should be kept smoke-free and safe from a fire that breaks out inside the living areas.

▲ Choose to build-in microwave ovens to avoid cluttering worktops.

The flat's own lobby or hallway behind its entrance door is the second line of defence in case of a fire. It offers a safety valve against smoke and fire spreading out from a room where it has begun. All of the rooms will be accessed from doors within this inner hallway, and these doors should also be fire-resisting.

It is worth stopping for a moment to consider why so much fire protection is needed when a building is divided up into flats because it generally is not when it is all in one occupation as a family home. Apartment buildings usually rely on a single escape staircase that all of the residencies lead off. Any self-contained apartment will have a kitchen and a lounge, the rooms where fires, when they do occur, often break out. It would be reasonable to assume that a building with three apartments has three times the fire risk as the same building as a single-family home with a single kitchen. Combine this increased risk with the living habits and patterns of different people, and the fact that without fire precautions a fire could occur in an apartment kitchen at ground level and grow to life-threatening status while the residents of the upstairs apartments slept on in blissful ignorance, and you begin to see why fire protection is such an issue.

As kitchens are the principal fire risk, it makes good sense to locate them in the furthest corner of the layout, whenever you can. That way you will not have to pass by them on the way out. Of course, the position of the drainage and the services in your building will determine the kitchen and bathroom locations more than anything else, but do not forget about noise and fire. Kitchens with all their appliances are a prime source of both of these, and those that are accessed via the entrance lobby and a fire door are not so much of a problem.

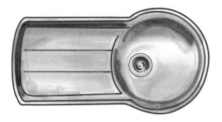

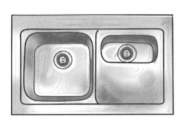

▲ Sink styles.

In an open-plan layout, the kitchenette must be at the furthest point from the door, as shown in the illustration on page 183. Creating a kitchen/diner is the obvious solution, or even a least a kitchen/diner/lounge where the cooking facilities are at the most remote part of the room. This kind of layout works well from a functional point of view, where meals and drinks can be prepared in the company of your guests. Often in small apartments the alternative is a tiny separate galley kitchen that is too cramped for more than one person at a time and isolated from the rest of the accommodation.

Modular design

Some inventive designs can reduce the average one-bedroom flat by as much as 70 per cent in area and still achieve a good standard of accommodation. If you have only 35–50 m² of floor area available, modular design is definitely for you. Severe space restriction will often mean dividing up a home into strips of narrow frontage. As long as you have depth in the building, this can work. Frontage gives you window or balcony space, and that makes everything possible. Depth gives you the challenge of finding a flexible internal layout and built-in storage (perhaps at high level, for example, so that it does not take up valuable floor space).

Kitchen modules (pods)

Where space is really restricted, you will be surprised how little floor area a kitchenette can take up. All that is often left for cooking is a small built-in oven or even a microwave oven, a sink and a fridge/freezer. Sinks might come in standard sizes, but fridge/freezers do not, and the smallest take up about 0.7 m² of floor space. Indeed, there are even modular kitchen units that meet all of your basic culinary needs in one fitting. The sort of thing you might find built into a caravan is now often used in studio apartments or indeed student accommodation where a separate room for the kitchen is not available. They are kitchen pods.

▲ A basic kitchen pod.

These flat-packed kitchens, when erected, plumbed and plugged in – for they come with sinks, electric hotplates and fridges – are a master class in space-saving engineering. They do not have extractor fans, and consequently these should be provided separately nearby, but otherwise all is contained in one piece of furniture. As an item of furniture, the kitchen module, or pod, does not fall into any of the definition of a kitchen I have seen. They are not a room at all, and yet they provide everything a studio flat or annexe needs in a space that is no bigger than a double wardrobe.

As with anything, you can choose the quality that you want. Some pods are available at the budget-end range and may not be as robust and serviceable as you would want in a tenanted apartment. In a normal kitchen, landlords expect to replace the worktops and door fronts every three years or so. That does not require a complete refit to the kitchen – just a makeover and at

▲ Kitchen pods come with built-in appliances as complete kitchens.

relatively modest expense. If you have to replace the entire kitchenette every three years, however, then clearly you have a lot more expense ahead of you and so it pays to buy quality.

The most robust modules have brushed stainless-steel surfaces and hardwearing timber doors in ash, alder or maple. Standard units are 1000 mm or 1200 mm in length, so not only do they suit studio apartments, but annexes for independent relatives can benefit from them as well.

It is not just kitchen pods that help when you need to maximize layout. Bathroom pods are also valuable, although many manufacturers have been producing space-saver designs for cloakrooms and en-suites for some time, and they are often compact enough.

Heating design

If installing an underfloor heating system is too much trouble when you are faced with timber-suspended floors already overdressed with sound- and fireproofing, I do not blame you. A conventional radiator system is definitely going to be less trouble. There is great choice now for radiator design and, for the high-end apartment, some luxury designer 'rads' can be a feature in their own right. Some actually look like apiece of modern art climbing the wall, while others can form a continuous plinth above the skirting.

Radiator styles

Compact
The most popular style of radiator are these compact convection types that come with a fitted flat-top grille and side end panels. Aesthetically, they are the most suitable because they hide the fins that a double panel radiator displays, making them look a lot tidier. You pay a little more for this, but it is well worth it for the improved appearance and the avoidance of a permanent dust trap.

Steel panel convectors
The industry's basic product, this is the standard pressed steel radiator that you can paint yourself or, more commonly now, buy factory-finished. The top and the sides are open between the

panels, allowing dust to collect there. The fins emit most of the heat by convection, but they do not look so good from the side or above when you can see them, as you can with these.

Tubular towel rail (not illustrated)

Tubular towel rails tend to have an electric element option, but it is simply that – an option. If you do not wish to or are unable to extend the central heating system to a bathroom, then the immersion heater option is at your disposal. The water-filled radiator is then heated by this electric element instead of the boiler. All that is needed is a fused connection unit within the electrical system (not a plug point).

Using a towel rail radiator to heat a large bathroom or, come to that, a small badly insulated bathroom is a common mistake – they are not capable of it. The rated output of these models is often low (often only 500 to 750 watts), and that is not measured with a towel draped over them. In the use they were intended, the heat given off to warm the room is often negligible.

COMPACT

Panel and towel rail

These models tend to work a little better than simple tubular towel rails if you want to heat a bathroom and warm a towel. They are a combination of a convector radiator and a single top rail extended from the face. Like conventional towel radiators, they are usually zinc-plated and powdercoat-finished, making them decorating-free and hence highly resistant to rust in damp conditions. Resist the urge to over paint them.

STEEL PANEL CONVECTOR

Flat panel

Once again, these types are used for interior design purposes. With a smooth front face instead of the usual vertical ribs, they can be more agreeable to look at. In reality, they are used more frequently in the heavy-duty range, where damage to them is more likely, such as in commercial and public buildings.

Low surface temperature

The safety radiator that we see in nursery schools and retirement homes may be desirable in your

PANEL AND TOWEL RAIL

annexe for the same reason. Although they do not look any different, they have a preset thermostatic control that prevents the radiator from reaching a hot-to-touch temperature. With boilers producing water at up to 60°C, standard radiators can reach surface temperatures of 50°C or more – hot enough to cause burns. As the elderly are a lot more vulnerable in this respect, these models are ideal for granny annexes.

Calculating the size of traditional radiators

All radiators are tested with a flow water temperature coming in of 75°C, a return temperature coming out of 65°C and an air temperature in the room of 20°C, and their rated outputs in the catalogue are based on these figures. A bit like the car fuel performance figures quoted by the makers, you cannot rely on them for actual performance and, when heating engineers design a system, they usually make an allowance for this fact. In practice, knocking 15 per cent off of the published output will see you nearer to finding the right size.

For conventional heating systems, heat losses from a room have to be calculated to size the radiators and, for underfloor heating, to decide on the pipe spacing. Radiators are sized by output by the manufacturer and can be chosen once the results of heat loss calculations are at hand. The heat loss calculation can be complex and precise, but a simplified version of it is often used for heating system design. You may not know exactly what your walls and windows are constructed of to be able to calculate an exact rate of heat transfer through them (known as a U-value), but the simplified approach will suffice.

The table below gives examples of the U-values for different elements. To calculate the total heat loss, it is simply a case of multiplying each area by the relevant U-value.

The temperature difference that is needed in the heat loss calculation is the difference between the inside and outside temperature through the structure, whether it be a roof, wall or floor. For an external bedroom wall, for example, you might consider the worst outside temperature to be −5°C and therefore the temperature difference for a bedroom wall is 23°C – the sum of 18 − (−5).

If the wall is internal within the apartment, the temperature difference may not exist. With an unheated common hallway or a party wall with another dwelling, however, the temperature on the other side is usually taken as 10°C. This low figure allows for the adjoining property to be unheated or unoccupied at a time when your apartment is.

U-VALUE EXAMPLES

External walls

	U-VALUE	TYPICAL CONSTRUCTION
Solid wall	1.60	215mm brickwork
Pre-1965 cavity wall	1.00	2-skin brickwork
1965–1984 built	0.75	1 skin brickwork + 1 skin blockwork
1985–1990 built	0.60	1 skin brickwork + 1 skin thicker thermal blockwork
1991–2002 built	0.45	1 skin brickwork, 50-mm cavity insulation and 1 skin blockwork
2002–2005 built	0.35	as above but 75-mm cavity insulation
2006–	0.30	as above but 100-mm cavity insulation

Roofs

	INSULATION FIBREGLASS	U-VALUE
	100-mm insulation	0.45
	150-mm insulation	0.35
	200-mm insulation	0.25
	100-mm + 150-mm insulation	0.18
	150-mm + 150-mm insulation	0.15

Ground floors

	U-VALUE
Uninsulated	0.70
80-mm phenolic foam insulated	0.30
50-mm expanded polystyrene insulated	0.45

Windows

U-VALUE		TYPICAL CONSTRUCTION
Double glazing		
Pre–1990	3.3	6-mm cavity
1990–2002	2.8	16-mm cavity
2002–2005	2.0	low e-glass 20-mm cavity
Post-2006	1.8	low-e glass/argon fill 20-mm cavity
Single glazing	5. 6	

Heat loss

The total heat loss from the apartment has as much to do with its ventilation as it does its construction and insulation levels. Losses have to be added on for ventilation, internal walls and ceilings as well. You cannot dispense with ventilation. As airtight as our homes have to be, we still need to breathe, and air changes are an essential part of our health. In habitable rooms, we have to allow for one and a half times the volume of the room to be replaced every hour. In kitchens, bathrooms, WCs and hallways, that figure is increased to twice the volume every hour. The air that has been so expensively heated up will, of course, have become stale, and we will need some fresh air brought in from the outside to replace it. Air that once again will need heating. The process of air changing is a slow and continuous one for much of the time, with background ventilation working 24/7 to do the work quietly. Every so often, a door or a window will be opened wide to rapidly purge the room of stale air and replace it with fresh. Such events are averaged out over the course of a normal day into the volume changes per hour we see above.

The calculation of heat loss, then, can only be done in two parts, the sum of which represents the total heat lost from the room. The first part is the heat exiting through the fabric, the walls, floor, windows and roof:

area (m²) x temperature differential (°C) x U-value (W/(m/K)) = heat loss (watts) – **1**

The second part is the heat lost through air changes, as ventilation loss.

air changes (no.) x room volume (m³) x temperature differential (°C) x vent factor* (W/(m³.°C) = heat loss (watts) – **2**

Note: * Vent factor is 0.33 W/m³.°C (taken to calculate the heat loss due to infiltration or mechanical extractor fans)

Total design heat loss is the sum of **1** and **2**.

Heat loss (watts)/floor area (m²) = heat required (w/m²) = select radiator

Heating and plastic plumbing

Copper has become very expensive recently and, luckily, it is no longer needed for water pipes – plastic pipe is firmly established now. A separate grade of plastic is made for heating and hot-water systems that is reinforced with perhaps five layers of cross-linked polyethylene and an oxygen barrier in the centre, sandwiched by the inner and outer layers. This oxygen barrier prevents air from leaking into the system and increases its longevity as a result. Plastic pipe does not heat up like copper does, and with this reduced conductivity comes insulation value,

SURFACE ELEMENT	AREA	X	TEMP / DIFF	X	U VALUE	=	DESIGN HEAT LOSS	TOTALS
	(m²)		(oC)		(W/m² oC)		Watts	
External wall	5.5	x	19	x	0.92	=	96	
Window	4	x	19	x	5	=	190	
Party Wall	10.0	x	8	x	2.1	=	190	
Internal wall 1	7.5	x	nil	x	n/a	=	n/a	
Internal wall 2	10.0	x	-2	x	1.7	=	-34	
Floor	12.0	x	-5	x	1.36	=	-82	
Ceiling	12.0	x	19	x	0.34	=	78	416

(1)

Ventilation Heat loss								
Air Changes	x	Room volume	x	Temp / Diff	x	Vent Factor	=	Design Heatloss
2	x	30	x	19	x	0.33	=	376
Total Design Heat loss								792 W

(2)

meaning that it does not lose so much heat as the water travels around the property. Even so, in cold areas such as roof spaces and floor voids, it should be insulated in exactly the same way as copper pipe, with foam pipe lagging.

Plastic hot-water pipes are also quieter than copper ones and, even when air pockets occur in the system, the pipes do not resonate with the pressure waves. You can afford to have some contact between them and timber joists, for example, whereas with copper you cannot. Copper pipes have to be separated by sufficiently deep notches in the floor timbers to ensure that they do not rub against the underside of floorboards, causing charring or creaking with friction as they expand and contract. Plumbers are renowned for not doing this. I lifted some chipboard flooring in my house that had spent 22 years in contact with a section of copper pipe feeding a radiator, to find that the board had been charred black and burnt halfway through. The plumber had not used any of the insulating wrap that is essential under and around pipes in contact with wood.

What was once a push-fit joint in the early days has become a push-and-twist lock joint now, which means that you can dismantle it if you get the wrong fitting – you just cannot reuse it without it leaking. Everybody has to try this for themselves because nobody likes to create waste (they are not cheap), but it simply does not seem to work – they are a one-fit-only product. Inside the fitting to which the pipe end itself will be pushed is a thin stainless-steel ring with teeth known as a 'collet'. This collet bites into the pipe when the joint is made, gripping it and preventing it being pulled out. Further inside the fitting is the O-ring that seals the joint to watertightness simply by being a very snug fit. To avoid us thinking that the pipe is all the way in when it is not, a system of marks made at intervals along it means that, if it is cut along one of these, when pushed fully home it should align with the next mark on the pipe. A bit of pressure is needed in pushing them in, but they do go convincingly with this after the initial resistance and you do feel confident (well, sort of) that it will be watertight.

If you have squashed the pipe or deformed it when cutting it to length, this seal will not be good enough and the joint will leak. If it gets squashed by some loading on the side later on it could still leak, and so the makers of these products have come up with a pipe insert as a sort of reinforcement to stiffen up the end of the pipe inside the fitting.

The pipe (or cable, as they sometimes call it) in the DIY ranges is often more rigid than in the professional ranges. That lack of flexibility is not helpful when it comes to bending it around things. Plastic pipe has a bending limit and, when you exceed it, without warning it kinks and the kink never comes out. To encourage it through bends without kinking, proformas can be used to sit the pipe in. This pipe does not like to stay where it is put as much as copper does, and I cannot emphasize enough the need for clips if you are not retaining it through holes bored in joists and studs.

If plastic plumbing has a fault it will I suspect be something to do with the joints and how well they age. Either that, or how well they can avoid being eaten by rats and mice. Rodents have a fondness for plastic, and they love to inhabit the secret places in our buildings where we run pipework. If you think you have a good chance of these creatures moving in, perhaps plastic pipes are not for you, unless you can run them inside metal ducts, of course – but that sort of defeats the object.

▾ Exploded view of plastic pipe coupling showing o-ring and collet inside.

Room thermostats

Sealed room thermostats are made for wet areas, such as bath and shower rooms. With these and the other standard room thermostats, you can control the temperature of each circuit independently, splitting the apartment into heating zones. To meet the minimum standards of the Building Regulations, at least two zones should be created.

Plasterboards and plastering

Never before have so many grades of plasterboard been manufactured. There is a board for every situation, and dividing up a home will require you to use most of them.

Apartment conversions eat plasterboard, and it is without question the number-one material on site. Along with the standard plasterboard, we now have fire-resistant board, sound-resistant board, moisture-resistant board, thermal insulation board and vapour-resistant foil-backed board. To help everyone identify which board is which, a colour-coding scheme has been adopted which thankfully seems to have been adopted universally.

Fire-resistant board   PINK
Sound-resistant board   BLUE
Moisture-resistant board   GREEN

Without this, the products would appear identical in situ. The edges of foil-backed boards show the silver aluminium foil extended so that it may be turned up beneath the board.

Insulation-backed boards have been around since the late 1980s, but have always been expensive and never widely used in my experience. They require a good thickness of the backing insulation to be able to achieve the insulation U-values of today, and that has made the boards unwieldy to handle and difficult to store. It is true that both plasterboard and rigid insulation in sheets of 2.88 m x 1. 44 m (from the imperial 8 x 4 ft) are unwieldy anyway, but adding the two together makes it harder still, and so most people seem to prefer to use the materials separately to achieve the same end result.

They generally comprise of ordinary 9.5-mm plasterboard bonded with a layer of phenolic foam insulation and often a built-in vapour barrier. Nothing less than 50 mm is much use any more, and so manufacturers have mostly stopped producing the thinner insulation boards that they previously made. Typical thermal resistance values for these products tend not to change much because of the consistency of the materials.

Here are some examples of what U-values you can expect:

INSULATION BONDED PLASTERBOARD			
Dimensions (R-value)	Thermal resistance* (U-value)	Thermal transmittance	
Thickness**	Board Size	K/w	W/(mK)
50 mm	1200 x 2400 mm	1.80	0.36
60 mm	1200 x 2400 mm	2.32	0.31
65 mm	1200 x 2400 mm	2.55	0.29

* Thermal transmittance (U-value) given is calculated upon lining a 215-mm-thick brick wall, plastered internally.

** Board thickness includes 9.5-mm-thick plasterboard bonded to phenolic foam insulation.

Thistle plaster

A wide variety of thistle plasters are now available depending on the finish required and the surface to which you are plastering. Some are single-coat plasters, while others are two-coat plasters needing an undercoat application first. All have varying coverage from a 25-kg standard bag, and the table below will give you some idea of how much you will need based on an 11-mm thickness to walls of undercoat and a 2-mm thickness of topcoat. The one-coat system provides 13 mm in one application and has proved popular for applying direct to aerated-block inner walls. Ceilings should have a reduced thickness of 8 mm at most.

Restoring historical and decorative plastering

The Georgians started the process of decorating ceilings with timber carvings, but that proved too expensive for the mass building of the Victorian age. To save money, the Victorians used plaster for their internal gentrification work, and so it is not just listed buildings that can have features worth retaining. Many ordinary Victorian homes have deep cornicing and ceiling roses, or plaster arches inside the narrow entrance halls.

The first thing that strikes you when you realize that you have to soundproof floors where you have these features is that you are going to lose them. It would be easy to, particularly when the ceiling height is high and you can lower it with the new sound-resistant ceiling, but you cannot add on layers of plasterboard inside the cornicing and expect it to look the same afterwards.

COVERAGE FOR TOPCOATS AND UNDERCOATS			
	Coverage	Drying time	Background
(25-kg bag)			
Topcoats			
Renovating finish plaster		10.5 m²	2 hrs
Replastering			
Plaster finish	10.5 m²	2 hrs	Any undercoat
Board finish	10.5 m²	1.5 hrs	Plasterboard
Multi-finish	10.5 m²	1.5 hrs	Multipurpose
Undercoats			
Renovating	3 m²	1.5–2 hrs	Replastering
Bonding	2.75 m²	1.5–2 hrs	Low-suction
Browning	3.5 m²	1.5 –2 hrs	Medium-suction
Universal one-coat	2.25 m²	1.5–2 hrs	General
Hardwall	3 m²	1.5–2 hrs	General

If you want to keep it as a feature, you are going to have to work on the soundproofing from above and either leave or restore the original plasterwork for all to enjoy. That can be done by raising the floorboards on the floor above, insulating between the joists and building up the new floor with one of the proprietary systems available. You may not be able to avoid lifting the level of the floorboards slightly in completing this work, and that will mean trimming doors down, but if the ceilings are that much of a feature it is worth all the effort.

Do not be tempted to restore the ceiling features until after the floor work is complete and the sound testing is done. Only then will you have found out how much repair has to be done. Missing sections that have lost their key and fallen away, cracks that need repairing – all can be worked at the decorating stage when the building work is finished.

Some cornices could be drawn out with a wooden block mould in situ, but other ceiling features such as roses around lights and the like were formed in moulds and stuck on later. Not all, though, as plasterers had a habit of making their own tools for carving out or impressing plaster before it set in place. Some of the sculptural beauty of plaster features are lost over time beneath the layers of paintwork and chips, but it is possible to restore them to near-original condition. Some plastering restoration specialists exist who use similar methods of dexterity and skill to renovate plasterwork. Missing pieces of plasterwork can be replaced by taking a rubber 'squeeze' of the remaining ornament and casting a new section from the mould, or by 're-running' a coving or cornice length.

Not all decoration in period homes is plaster. Some of it could be powdered chalk and linseed oil mixed together as a cheap alternative, or even papier-mâche. The mix of the plaster in a period home will have been decided upon by the availability of local materials as much as anything else. Sand needed to be good quality and not salty or silty. Animal by-products used in the mix might vary from horse or goats' hair to cow dung and even blood. Other binding agents included cheese and straw chopped up into fine pieces.

Most of the art went out of plasterwork early in the twentieth century after the Edwardian era, but now that plaster has taken back over from plastic paint, decorative plasterwork for ceilings is becoming popular once again. An original period feature, whether restored or in its original condition, has to be worth preserving. Be patient, with careful finishing, the blemishes should be filled and lost when the plasterer is complete. If you do have a high-enough ceiling level to achieve it, getting the accent lighting right to display it will be important once the work is done. A chandelier-style light in the centre or carefully placed plaster-wall uplighters always work well, but please keep the recessed spotlights for new ceilings.

If you do not have the budget to restore the plaster cornicing, the best you can do is encapsulate it. Concealing historical and indeed archaeological features is a recognized way of preserving them. The suspended ceiling approach is not a bad one at all. A false ceiling supported by new joists from the walls and entirely independent of the existing one will leave the concealed features untouched for future generations to uncover. Who knows, one day we might all be in the business of making homes bigger again and undividing them, and what a joy it will be for those people to uncover the original features.

Restoring stucco on external façades

In town centres, large properties over shops have often been left neglected. Until the recent drive to find low-cost housing in apartment conversions, the floors above the high-street stores were often left for storage of goods or just simply left. Now, however, planning policies have changed, and many of these spaces are being put to good residential use.

They do tend to have excellent façades, although many are getting a little old now and have been neglected for too long. At the very least external façades need inspecting, and often it is not until a scaffold is erected that it becomes possible to see what repairs are needed. Sandstone and limestone were often used to describe features in stucco onto prominent buildings, but these are soft stones that erode with time and weather. Before that, stucco rendering was popular in the late eighteenth and early nineteenth centuries. It was intended to imitate stone and designed to be a hard surface that utilized Roman cement to that aim (Portland Cement did not usurp it until the middle of the nineteenth century). Time has run out now for most of these façades, and many need to be repaired or replaced. You may need to enlist the help of some specialist advisers and contractors to do it.

With elevations restored, apartment buildings can look grander than they are, dramatically increasing the value of the smallest of homes within. When space over one floor is not enough, however, maisonettes can provide you with so much more and, in doing so, solve some of the problems that come with apartments by having a private entrance all of their own.

CHAPTER 7

Maisonettes fall somewhere between being apartments and houses. In fact, by definition they are small houses with their own external entrance door. It is that door that strictly distinguishes a maisonette from being an apartment, the entrance of which is from common space inside the building. There is, however, a more obvious difference – maisonettes usually cover two floors. A third floor might start to make them too large and more of a town house or a mews house (where the accommodation is built over a garage.)

A maisonette can be designed to a contemporary open-plan layout rather than the traditional separated rooms and doors, but let's start by taken a look at the traditional layout.

Access

A four-storey home can usually be split in two, with the top two floors becoming one maisonette and the lower two floors becoming another. Invariably, the lower property would have a separate entrance, perhaps at the rear, and the upper one would be accessed via the front door and a stairway leading up. In this sense, the staircase is private and within the maisonette, and consequently exempt from reverberation sound requirements. The stair enclosing wall, however, would separate the two homes, and that means it will need both sound and fire resistance, a task that is not easy to achieve on stairs where the width cannot be encroached upon. In these situations, pretty much all of the work to upgrade the wall must be done on the lower maisonette's side, where the space can be obtained.

If you were thinking of the same arrangement with a studio flat or one-bedroom apartment at ground level and a separate private stair rising from the entrance to a maisonette above, you may have to think again. In mixing the divided building between maisonette and apartment, you will usually be encouraged to form the maisonette at ground level. As it happens, most planning authorities like to see the largest units in a dividing building on the ground floor. The ground floor with its garden access is ideal for families. If you have the choice over three floors of creating a maisonette over two of them and an apartment on the other, then the maisonette would generally have to occupy the ground and first floor, and the apartment the second.

Estate agents being what they are, I have often seen large apartments described incorrectly as maisonettes. If the entrance door opens from a common space that serves other homes in the building, then you are not talking about a maisonette, no matter how small that common space may be. It is that common space that makes all the difference, and the entrance door will have to be at least FD30S standard.

Ordinarily, the front door of a maisonette is no different from that of any house. If you do not fancy a solid wood external door, you now have the choice of a composite or PVC-u door (see page 000). Frankly, PVC-u doors were always grotesque. The proportions for frame width and door panels were all wrong, and they looked too much like the sealed hatch doorways you find in submarines. Even now that the thresholds have been reduced to make them accessible for people with disabilities, they still have fallen out of vogue. Replacing them is the finer detailing of the composite door, which appears similar if not identical to a wooden one, thanks to a metal face pressed with a woodgrain effect. Composite doors have an insulated core to keep the warmth in and excellent brush seals to the frame. Alas, they have one drawback: they are easily damaged – dented, to be precise. The repair process for them is similar to that for car bodies and, when it comes down to it, uses the same filler.

With the luxury of a classy front door comes a choice of ironmongery and, unlike apartments with fire-rated doors, there are no restrictions on it. Instead you can focus on things such as security and locking yourself out unexpectedly. Some composite front doors have lever handles outside that will not deadlock when you shut the door behind you and leave the key indoors, but this does mean you have to lock yourself in to prevent unwelcome visitors joining you. This of course means that you cannot get out without the key, and that is not great in an emergency.

Layout

In the case of the true maisonette, it is often not necessary to have fire-rated doors at all, as the layout is often no different from that of a house, but as it happens fire-rated doors can be very handy when planning the layout. Even so, you have to the find room for a staircase if one does not exist at present and enclose it to the entrance door. The landing and hallway achieved by doing this must serve the rooms and, as convention would have it, the living room and kitchen would be on the entrance level and the bedrooms and bathroom on the other.

Do not locate the kitchen near the front door – it should still reside in a distant corner. You might even choose to switch the floors around and have the bedrooms on the entrance storey and the living rooms and kitchens on the next. This upside-down approach can work well if the entrance floor is the uppermost

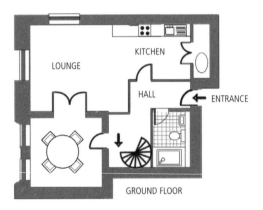

▸ Typical two-bed maisonette with separated plan layout.

(ground) and the other is the basement (below ground) level. The occupants will buy into your design more in this case, rather than facing a regular trip upstairs to the lounge etc. From a services viewpoint, the bathroom needs to be above the kitchen, or vice versa; the location of external walls and drainage comes into play.

As with studio flats and apartments, a basic design strategy has been developed when it comes to fire safety, but flexibility of design is increasingly on offer if you are prepared to use alternative escape routes, risk assessment or sprinkler system protection. In a maisonette, as in an apartment, the occupants need to be able to turn their backs on a fire and escape away from it, a requirement that is easier to meet in the layout of maisonettes, where there is a wide frontage or both a front and rear door. If you find yourself in the same room as the fire, being able to escape from that room is something that has to be planned for in the design. Clearly you are not going to be able to eliminate the risk entirely of anyone perishing in a fire, but by design you can reduce that risk to a great extent and down to a level where the odds are stacked in favour of the occupant's survival.

Whether the entrance door is at the front or back of the building, entering through it should find you in an inner hallway, with the staircase leading up or down to the other level and doors leading off to the entrance-level rooms. Each of the habitable rooms has an enclosing wall and door that feeds off of a hallway or landing. When these doors are fire-rated, the maisonette's level above the ground can be raised above the 4.5-m limit (see page 000), as long as you create an alternative exit that is not a window, but rather a way of bypassing the fire to get to the staircase, down and out. That could be a 'pass' door; if you can plan one in without too much disruption, that is the most favoured approach. An external balcony that links to another or the ground by a fire escape stair is another. Admittedly, these are often not an option, and so the rooms have to be planned to create an alternative route out of the maisonette that is remote enough and fire-protected enough to be considered as a proper alternative.

Walls and doors help enormously in these situations. Indeed, the ideal scenario from a fire-safety point of view is to have every room served by two doors on opposite walls. The creation of a maze inside the dwelling may not seem like a brilliant idea, but in fact the more choices you have for escaping a fire, the greater your chance of escape.

Open-plan layouts

With the staircase located within rooms instead of the entrance hall, the layout becomes open plan. It is even more essential in the open-plan layout to push the kitchen to the far corner. When the staircase is located in the lounge and without protection, it really needs to be on the other floor to the entrance floor, thus giving the bedrooms the opportunity to be nearest to the exit. With most fires breaking out in kitchens, you do not want the front door in or next to the kitchen area, where you have to pass through it to escape.

It may not even be enough to locate the kitchenette in a corner of the entrance floor, when the other habitable rooms are upstairs and even further away from the front door. If that is your chosen layout, the windows may have to serve as escape routes and that depends on their size. It means that those rooms not on the entrance level should have their own escape route, particularly bedrooms, as we are most at risk when we are asleep.

Using windows as exits is a little unnatural, but in practice they are the last resort and usually what distinguishes a successful rescue and an unsuccessful one. For a window to be an available option, the opening must be big enough and accessible enough. Window escape sizes are measured as clear space 450 mm wide by 450 mm high, but also at least 0.33 m² in area. Those are minimum sizes and something larger is always preferable. The 450-mm clear width means a 600-mm wide casement in reality, to allow for the actual casement encroaching on the opening, even when it is open.

There are other constraints on using windows as fire exits. As you might expect, these are limits on the height of the floor above the ground outside. Ladder rescue is possible only at certain levels and, although the Fire Brigade has equipment that can reach much higher, escape heights are also based on basic ladder rescue, and that could be by neighbours as well as by the emergency services. The maximum height quoted in the approved guidance is 4.5 m above ground level, but that measure is not to the windowsill – it is to the floor below it. You can add on another 800 mm to reach sill height, then consider how happy you would be about leaving your home via the window at this altitude; clearly it will make a difference if the room behind you is on fire. It does, however, mean that the higher ceiling heights found in a large Victorian home put only the first floor within the limit; a second floor is usually above it. This is another good reason for keeping the maisonette at ground- and first-floor level, particularly if you want freedom of design and an open-plan layout. With escape exit windows, the bedrooms on that upper level can now be reached from a staircase that feeds down into a room below, and the only compartmentation you will need will be for privacy, to separate the bedrooms from each other and the bathroom. In a one-bedroom maisonette with en-suite bathroom, the possibility of having the entire space open plan materialises.

I have seen some strange designs with maisonettes – layouts where bedrooms are divided off by partitions that act more like screens than walls, as they do not make it all the way across the room; bathrooms that are in the bedroom and entirely unscreened. If this kind of flowing open-plan design is for you, your maisonette will need to be fairly close to the ground. The kitchen should be in the most remote part of the accommodation, but equally that can mean that it need not be enclosed with walls and a door, allowing for the chef to be in contact with everyone at the table. Imagine a rear-corner kitchen, perhaps on a raised dais platform, that leads off the dining area, which in turn leads off to the lounge at the front of the maisonette, nearest to the entrance hall.

Thermal insulation

Residing under a roof space has some advantages, not least of all the potential extra storage space. For residents, this and the fact that nobody is going to be thumping on the floor above you are the main attractions. For the home divider, the chance to hide away the plumbing and distribute services through the roof void is a bonus. With as much as half of the heat from a maisonette going skywards out through the roof, however, you need to make a better-than-average job of insulating it.

Glass-wool quilts are still good for this job, but I would now only use those that come ensleeved in a polythene or foil liner like a bed quilt. They also need to be laid in two layers. The liners prevent you from coming into contact with what has always been an unpleasant and arguably unhealthy material. The lined quilts are perforated with tiny holes to make them breathable to water vapour, and make rolling out the insulation, getting it into position and fluffing it up a whole lot easier. Given how unpleasant the task is otherwise, I am at a loss to explain why the manufacturers are not required to produce all mineral and glassfibre products in these bags. A layer in one direction, perhaps 150 mm thick, run out between the ceiling joists is not enough by itself, and so a second 150-mm layer should be run in the opposite direction over the top. You might use a combination of a 100 mm and 200 mm to suit your joist depth. but you should aim for a total thickness of 300 mm.

Storage space and access of any kind becomes a problem now, unless you build up a small deck platform as you would for a water tank. The storage deck needs to be raised sufficiently to avoid it squashing the insulation down, which will reduce its quality. If you have 100-mm deep ceiling joists, 200-mm deep bearers will need to be run across them in the opposite direction to clear the insulation. Given the weight of these timbers and the weight of storage and access, it is essential that you consider the strength of the ceiling beforehand. A structural engineer can calculate exactly what stresses are being exerted on the ceiling for you, and design a storage deck. I have yet to see anyone do it, but raised storage platform materials are available in lightweight aluminium systems and TJI joists made by trussed-rafter manufacturers. They would provide a raised deck structure that is lighter than solid wood, but strong enough for some light storage, without squashing or breaking the insulation layer.

If you do use solid timber, 38-mm wide bearers will be sufficient to create the deck, and these should spread across at least four joists (ideally more), to distribute the load. Spacing them at 600-mm centres will allow a 22-mm thick chipboard deck. Before the decking boards are positioned, though, noggins will need to be fixed between the bearers to prevent them rotating; 100 mm x 50 mm timbers should be used for this, or off-cuts of the bearers if you have them. It is always wise to keep your storage space and your deck size to a minimum – ceilings and roof voids have never actually been designed for storage. Restrict the area covered by the deck to around the loft hatch where things are in reach without you having to get into the roof space and walk about, placing undue pressure on the deck.

Upgrading thermal insulation

Even if you do not plan to reline the external walls, depending on the age and construction of the building, some upgrading of them may be required to bring up their thermal insulation values. A threshold limit was introduced to the Building Regulations in 2006, and elements that fall below it should be upgraded. The

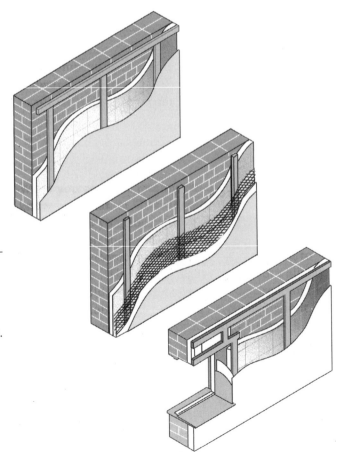

▶ Internal dry-lining fixed to timber battens with insulation board between.

threshold U-values and required new U-values are likely to change to tackle carbon emissions from housing, but the rough guide below will give an idea of what values can be obtained.

Relining the external walls of the new home cannot be avoided unless they are insulated already to a U-value of at least 0.7 w/m.k (this is the thermal conductivity of a material). This threshold value means that anything higher is so poorly insulated that it must be upgraded to reduce heat loss and therefore carbon emissions. A higher U-value could equate to a cavity wall with brickwork outside and 100-mm concrete blockwork inside, but no insulation in between, and in this case the cavity could be injected with blown-fibre insulation to raise the U-value considerably (perhaps to 0.35 w/sq.m.k.

For solid walls it will be a case of losing some floor space and lining the inner faces again. Timber battens to form a studwork frame can be erected inside, and these can be used to run new cables and pipes, as well as insulated between to make a warm lining. A solid brick wall 215 mm thick will achieve a U-value of about 1.60. To raise it to 0.31 will require 50 mm of rigid polyurethane foam board insulation between the timber framework of CLS (Canadian Lumber Standard) studs (which should be at 600-mm centres).

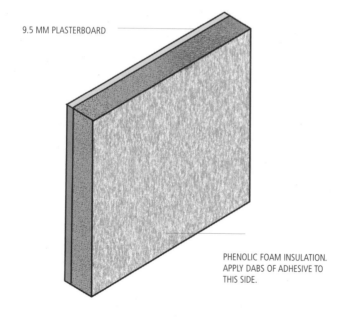

9.5 MM PLASTERBOARD

◀ Plasterboard backed with phenolic foam insulation can be used for internal lining. Fix it with dabs of adhesive.

PHENOLIC FOAM INSULATION. APPLY DABS OF ADHESIVE TO THIS SIDE.

ROUGH GUIDE TO IMPROVING U-VALUES

External walls	Existing U-value	Insulate with:	New U-value
Solid wall	1.60	50-mm phenolic foam boards internal, plaster-board and set	0.31
Pre-1965 cavity wall	1.00	Cavity-fill injection of PUF	0.40
1965–1984 built	0.75	Cavity-fill injection of blown fibre	0. 40
1985–1990 built	0.60	Cavity-fill injection of blown fibre	0.35
1991–2002 built	0.45	25-mm phenolic foam boards internal, plasterboard and set	0.25
2002 – 2005 built	0.35	–	–

Roof spaces	Existing U-value	Add to achieve a U-value of 0.16
Uninsulated	–	Glassfibre quilt 150 mm between joists plus 150 mm above
100-mm insulation	0.45	Glassfibre quilt 200 mm above joists
150-mm insulation	0.35	Glassfibre quilt 150 mm above joists
200-mm insulation	0.25	Glassfibre quilt 100 mm above joists
100-mm plus 150-mm insulation	0.18	n/a

Ground floors*	Existing U-value	Insulate with:	New U-value
Suspended ground	0.70–1.0 floors –	100-mm phenolic foam	0.25
Joists @ 400 mm crs		Boards between joists	
Solid ground floors	0.70	70 mm phenolic foam boards, polythene screed finish	0.21

* assumes a P/A (perimeter of floor around external walls/floor area) ratio of 0.5

Windows	U-value
Double glazing	
Pre-1990	3.3
1990–2002	2.8
2002–2006	2.0
2006–2007	1.8
Single glazing	5. 6

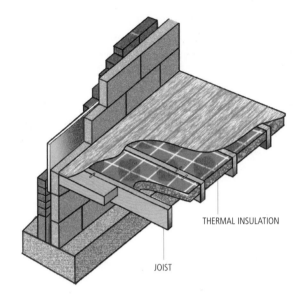

THERMAL INSULATION

JOIST

◄ Suspended timber floor with thermal insulation to increase energy savings.

Kitchen appliances

With the luxury of extra space comes the fully equipped kitchen, and maisonettes can usually afford a separate room for them. Once you have fitted dishwashers, washing machines and tumble driers whirring away, you want to be able to shut the door on them if you can. Kitchen space, though, depends not so much on whether you can get everything into fitted cupboards and beneath the worktops, but on whether you can operate them afterwards. Show homes have a reputation for sometimes revealing that, although the kitchen has been planned and installed, well appointed does not necessarily mean you can get to everything. A cooker door that will not open fully because it hits a door handle, a dishwasher door that should drop down fully for loading and emptying that cannot because the cupboards on the other side prevent it – these sorts of things are surprisingly common. They worked on the drawing board, but not in three-dimensional reality. Appliances need more space than they occupy – space for you to move around them and use them. Once you add these factors, you start to see how big kitchens have to really be.

Take full advantage of those gadgets such as carousel units and swing bins that fit inside corner cupboards and provide storage solutions. Squeezing into a galley kitchen with only 600 mm between opposite worktops and units is not fun and requires a lot of choreography if more than one person is in the room. At least 1 m of clear space in front of any cupboard or appliance is essential.

And so the extra space that comes with a maisonette brings some freedom of design and lifestyle. Instead of a tiny kitchen or

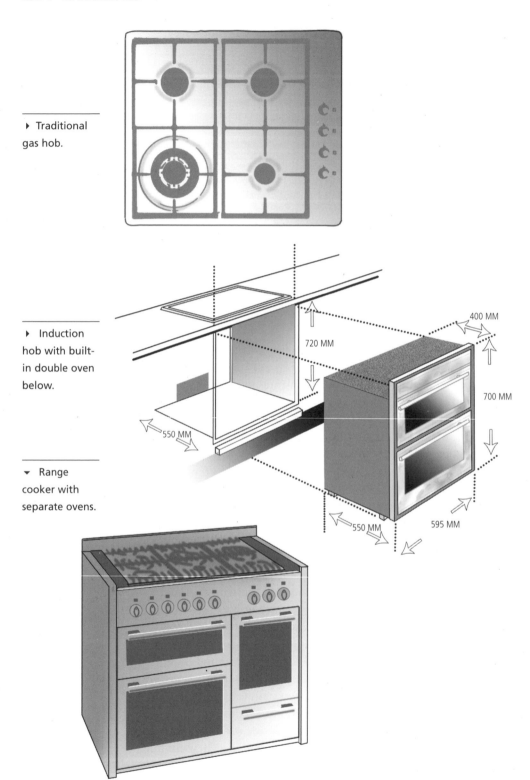

▸ Traditional gas hob.

▸ Induction hob with built-in double oven below.

▾ Range cooker with separate ovens.

a kitchenette corner in the lounge, a decent-sized kitchen is on the cards and, with it, the chance to have a full-size cooker. You cannot create space and not immediately fill it.

Ranges

For those of you who want to roast a whole pig or heat the maisonette from the kitchen, a range is all you need. I am told that, as they heat up the oven to a constant and even temperature, they cook things much more thoroughly and slowly than other cookers, to the point where your food tastes so much better. Ranges are becoming more and more popular in urban homes and have now moved out of the country and into our cities, too. With a range you now have a choice of fuels, from wood to gas and even electric. What's more, ranges are on offer now not just with a choice of fuel, but also with dual-fuel possibilities. Electric ovens and gas burners are popular – they give all the controllability of gas beneath a saucepan or frying pan, but the even heat of an electric grill and an electric oven.

With a gas-fired range, you have the opportunity to heat your maisonette as well as cook because they can come complete with an integrated central heating boiler. To comply with regulations, two separate burners are needed – one to serve the cooker and one to serve the heating and hot-water supply. In the original ranges, heating and cooking were done from one burner, into which you regularly shovelled wood or coal. If the kitchen and the range were at the heart of the house, as they often were, it heated the whole building and cooked your Sunday roast all at the same time. Not all ranges are solely fitted with slow-cook ovens; some also have fan-assisted ovens and rotisseries built in.

If you still cannot escape visions of a farmhouse kitchen range in matt black or British racing green, look again – you will see plenty of contemporary-styled ranges in stainless steel for the professional look. When I think of ranges and cookers, the difference to me is in the build quality – diamond-glazed interiors to the oven, cast-iron pan supports and griddles, solid iron oven door etc – and for all that quality and robustness you pay in four figures. A small gas cooker is much cheaper by comparison, but the knobs will fall off repeatedly and the electronic ignition will need replacing in a few years.

The gas and solid fuel models that rely on an open flue and combustion ventilation are fine for draughty old farmhouses, but not so great in the newly divided small home, but that no longer stops you. Today we have electric stoves that require no fluing or air supply. I have no idea whether gas would be cheaper to run,

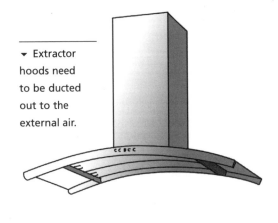

▼ Extractor
hoods need
to be ducted
out to the
external air.

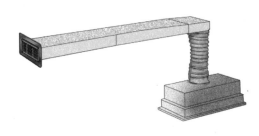

although I am certain a solid-fuel model would if you find the idea of chopping your own kindling before dinner romantic.

Any fuel other than electric is going to need air to the room in which you install it. This air is not for you to breathe, but for combustion, and it will ensure that the appliance stays lit and the flue gases go out through the flue. As it happens, the air will help you to continue breathing because flue gases contain carbon monoxide, a silent killer that you do not want spilling out into the room. Indeed, the risk of gas spillage occurring in a kitchen is always there and more so since we have become accustomed to installing an extractor fan. Extractor fans suck out the humid air – that's their job. But in so doing they can steal combustion air from the range, which helps to keep the range alight. Even tumble dryers can have fans built in that interfere with the flue gases. In any kitchen supplied with fuels other than electric, it is essential that your range installer carries out a spillage test on the appliance to ensure that it operates safely.

For this very reason many open-flued appliances such as ranges should not be located in the same room as extractor fans, and manufacturers of them are at great pains to tell you so. The regulations have for a while drawn attention to this problem and sometimes advised that fans with greatly reduced extract rates may be acceptable, but frankly it is best not to try to combine the two at all. Luckily, electric ranges have benefits that go beyond cooking.

For conventional cookers, extractor fans and air supply to the kitchen are essential, and most hobs now come with extractor hoods whether they are ceiling-mounted for cooking islands or wall-mounted. Most of these fans are more than capable of meeting the rapid ventilation standard, but bear in mind that the duct length will reduce performance and a single right-angle bend is the equivalent of more than a metre of straight duct. Manufacturers sometimes quote the maximum extraction rate in cubic metres per hour, which allows you to calculate the volume of your kitchen and multiply it by 10 (required air changes per hour) to match the performance to your needs. For example:

kitchen 4 m long x 3 m wide x 2. 5 m high = 30 m³ x 10 air changes per hour = 300

Larger diameter ducts will carry more air and achieve better exchange rates, but they also tend to be noisier. On maximum power, at more than 60 decibels of noise most will drown out conversation. Finding one less than 50 could be a challenge, but then again you do not need it on maximum for long.

Bathrooms

From the kitchen to the bathroom and, as with any two-storey home, it helps if one is directly above the other. Plumbing is made so much easier, and it also helps to reduce noise within the maisonette. Bedroom floors and walls need to be insulated against sound, but not to the same level as those separating homes. For internal sound insulation, only airborne sound is considered, and the measure for that is set at 40 decibels. Bathroom walls that divide the bathroom from bedrooms can meet this standard even if they are studwork partitions. It is only a matter of providing some sound insulation batts between the studs or an extra layer of plasterboard on both sides to double the thickness of the linings. This does not apply to en-suite bathrooms annexed to a bedroom. In fact, any door opening in the wall is going to make it pointless. For sanitaryware, the range of styles is growing and, again as with kitchens, you can pretty much spend as much as you want to on appliances and fittings. If the home is for let, a standard white contract suite will be adequate. In large Victorian buildings, a white suite with opulent chrome or brassware taps and high-level WC cisterns looks the part, but is only worth it if the home is to be kept for personal occupancy or sold. Victorian-style showers with surface-fixed riser pipes and single-lever capstans that drop a deluge of water from a large rose are less popular now than they were just a few years back, but they are always stylish and suit Victorian house divisions. Gold-finished taps and the like were out of vogue by the middle of the twenty-noughts and replaced by chrome finish. White and chrome dominate the market now, but I am sure that will change again soon.

Contemporary styles of glass bowl or stone basins, wood cabinets, and chrome accessories have been popular and ever changing in recent years, keeping them fresh and stylish. Contemporary bathrooms have curves and sweeping lines, but are simple and uncluttered with no fancy trims.

In the end, remember that maisonettes are, after all is said and done, still limited in space, and the bathroom is no place to be extravagant with floor area, at the expense of habitable rooms.

WCs

Close-coupled toilets are by far the most popular and I think partly because they use up less space. Without the flush pipe to bring the pan forwards, they are that extra bit compact and tidy. Flush pipes were never pretty anyway. Corner toilets are available for the space-saving en-suite, but at tremendous expense. The concealed cistern types look as though they save space, but tend not to, simply because the wall structure has to be built out to provide the cavity to hide the cistern and ends up taking more room in doing so than a conventional surface cistern.

Taps

Taps have been pieces of art for a while, and they continue to be. Half of the taps sold in the United Kingdom are imported, and pricewise you can pay what you like. It has to be said, however, that the same products in France, for example, are sold at a fraction of the price. The technology used in taps has not changed since washers were replaced by ceramic discs; all that has happened since about 1990 is that architecture has allowed taps to become designer products. They have become difficult to service and maintain now, and most, regardless of price, are ultimately disposable. Make sure that you fit service valves in line to the water pipes, which will make it easier to replace the taps when you have grown tired of their style. For a small basin, flow-reducer valves can be fitted, too. For me, though, the most stylish of taps is simply the hole in the ceiling. Pressing a button near the bath releases a stream of water from the ceiling directly above the bath to fill it. No actual taps exist.

Baths

My one tip here is to measure your stairs and door widths before you buy. Baths do not bend well around corners, and anything other than glassfibre is also heavy and awkwardly shaped. For heavy metal bathtubs, the floor structure may need strengthening with additional joists and exterior-grade plywood beforehand, if bathing is not to be heightened by the risk of a sudden change in floor level. The real weight problem comes with the cast-iron centrepiece roll-top bath for your Victorian home, but otherwise you should be safe to simply spread the load with bearers beneath the supports. You should provide a bath if you can, even if it is a short or narrow one. If the room is not big enough for a separate shower, a mixer-tap shower for the bath with screen is ideal. Steer clear of the cling-on curtain and fit an acrylic-hinged screen that fits to a rubber seal against the bath top, keeping it watertight at the shower end There are some baths designed for mixer-shower use with widened tap ends and curved acrylic screens enclosing them. They are the next best thing to a shower cubicle.

Showers

The shower has come a long way. It is no longer a case of simply getting wet all over; it can be a steam and body jet treatment as well, with shower cabins coming as complete plastic cubicles – directional body jets built in. As factory-made plastic units, they have the benefit of being leak-free – a precious commodity in a first-floor shower. For the developer and DIY enthusiast alike, the ease of installation counts for a lot with these cabins. You simply need to fix them to the wall and connect up the hot and cold water. They work best with unvented water systems, but do not forget just how much water they deliver. The average shower uses 35 litres of water compared to 90 litres in one of these, and your meter will spin. A little more space is needed than with a standard shower and a good deal more money, but for the top-end maisonette they are practically essential.

Building a shower

If you are not enchanted by the idea of showering in Tupperware and would like a more traditional feel to the shower, glazed wall tiles remain the favourite surface finish. With so much choice and the opportunity to find a really stylish and luxurious finish, I think only glass can compete. The problem is tiles have joints between them, and those joints are not waterproof, in spite of what it might say on that tin of grout. If you simply tile to a plasterboard-lined wall, it will soon become saturated and part company with the tiles. I have used WPB (waterproof bonded) grade plywood to line the shower walls beneath the tiling (do not use OSB sheets) and, although this performs much better when it gets wet, it still gets wet. If you go with the timber-backing board option, use ply in the thickest sheet you can – at least 9 mm thick but ideally more, and screw the board into position with stainless-steel screws.

I have lined plasterboard walls in this way using exterior-grade plywood and waterproofing adhesive, as well as screws to fix the plywood into position. The tiles I chose were very large, to reduce the amount of joints, and I used the best-quality grout I could find.

I also fixed the shower to the wall opposing the glass door so that the water would be directed away from the tiles to start with. If all this sounds paranoid to you, I can only suggest that you cannot go far enough to waterproof a shower. They are prone to leaking and need a belt-and-braces approach to avoid problems later.

There is an alternative material for the backing board that is not timber- or plaster-based. It is based on cement fibre and truly waterproof, but expensive for what it is, and it is still necessary to deal with the joints and edges in just the same manner because they are the weak points.

Mixer showers

Fuelled from a combi boiler to deliver continuous hot water (albeit at a low flow rate), a quality mixer shower should last a few years. The cheap ones do not. These need balancing when it comes to water pressure, so make sure that you have the access to fit service and flow-rate valves for maintenance.

Electric showers

The electricity supply cannot simply be taken from the ring main for most electric showers. With ring mains running at 30 amps and lighting circuits at 15 amps, they are inadequately rated, meaning that the electric shower should not be an afterthought. The electrician will need to know that it is proposed and the model intended for use. Showers tend to require 45-amp circuits, and that means a separate circuit back to the consumer unit. Before you go ahead with your shower installation project, check the consumer unit has a spare fuse that can provide this. If it does not, it will mean adding another unit or replacing the existing one with something larger.

When choosing the cable size for wiring an electric shower, the current carrying capacity achieved must be at least equal to that of the shower rating. For example, a 45-amp rating from a 10.5-kilowatt shower, with the cable buried in an insulated wall, will require a 16-mm^2 cable achieving a capacity of 57 amps. A 10-mm^2 cable in this instance would achieve only a 43-amp capacity. The trouble is, of course, if the cable has to run a long way back to the consumer unit, the chances are it will be encased in insulation somewhere and it is best to use a 16-mm^2 cable to cover this and stay safe. It is also worth mentioning that, if several cables are bundled together, the same effect as being encased by insulation can be produced and the derating factors should be used.

A 45-amp double-pole switch should be included in the circuit to isolate the supply when necessary, as well as an RCD (which may be on the consumer unit for this circuit). The double-pole switch needs to be placed above the outside of the bathroom door opening, so that it is not used by mistake or with wet hands. If you would rather not do this, your only other choice is a pull-cord ceiling-mounted switch for isolating. It can go inside the room. Whichever option you choose, the switch should have a neon indicator to reveal whether the supply is on or off. Remember that it must be impossible to touch the switch body while standing in the bath or shower for it to be correctly positioned.

Earth bonding

The combination of water and electricity is a lethal one, and the opportunity for electricity to short out through metal pipework and await the touch of wet hands is a dangerous one. Correct earth bonding is an essential element of electrical safety, and tests are conducted to determine its continuity. The earthing arrangement stems from the main earthing bar in the consumer unit. Only earth wires acting as the main equipotential bonding may run to metal water and gas service pipes, often at the point of the supply entry. It is not permitted for installation earthing to be connected to these and has not been since 1966. While all of the circuits will have earth wires connecting back to the main bar, special zones such as bathrooms should have extra bonding attached to water pipes, metal heating pipes for radiators, metal baths and basins, and other exposed conductive parts.

Special zones such as these attract more onerous requirements for wiring because of the increased risk. All exposed metal parts must be earth-bonded together using a sufficient-sized cable. The current edition of the IEE Wiring Regulations will give you the full details of what size cable and what bonding measures are required.

WASTE PIPE REQUIREMENTS				
Appliance	Waste pipe size	Maximum length	Trap size	Standard fall of waste (per metre)
WC	100 mm	6 m	50 mm	20 mm
Bath	40 mm	3 m	50 mm	20–40 mm
Shower	40 mm	3 m	50 mm	20–40 mm
Basin	32 mm	1.7 m	75 mm	20 mm
Combined	50 mm	4 m	–	20–40 mm

All electrical work in bathrooms and kitchens is 'notifiable' under the Building Regulations for compliance with Part P (England and Wales). This means that it will need to be designed, inspected, tested and approved. The best way to ensure this is by using an electrician that is registered under the government's competent persons scheme. The NICEIC and ECA (see Useful Contacts) will advise you of their registered members in your locality, but other bodies also exist.

Plumbing in waste pipes

Often the plumbing design is left to the final stages, as if it can be achieved one way or another, but you simply cannot assume that it will. Waste pipes will run only so far, and they need to have an adequate gradient on them, be properly supported and be accessible for cleaning blockages.

The fall on waste pipes of 32–50 mm in diameter should be somewhere between 18 mm and 90 mm per metre run. Outside of these limits problems are likely to occur. The larger the pipe, the shallower the allowable fall. With 100-mm pipes for WC pans, the fall should be at the lower gradient of 18 mm per metre for a single WC.

As the table shows, waste runs have limits if they are to remain ventilated and the water is to be maintained in the traps. If they exceed these limits, the branches need added vents or air admittance valves must be installed that can draw air in on demand. These devices draw air into the system when it is needed, to aid the flow of water and protect the traps. You can buy them as 100-mm fittings to go on top of stub stacks (shortened soil vent pipes) or as smaller diameters to go on bath and basin waste pipes. They are very useful on 40-mm shower wastes where en-suite showers are being installed some distance from the existing

▾ 40 mm pipe diameter branch waste vented by an air admittance valve.

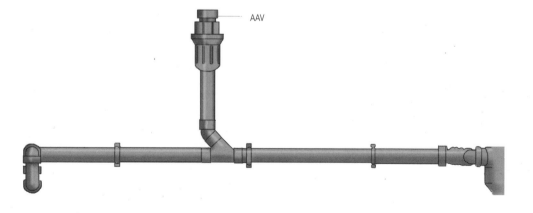

AAV

drainage system and the pipe run would exceed 3 m.

For basins and sinks, anti-vacuum traps can be fitted with miniature air admittance valves on them. I have used them on both a kitchen sink and a vanity basin, and both have worked flawlessly. Hiding them in a cupboard beneath the appliance is essential, though. These products have a rubber seal inside them that could freeze up if fitted outside, so you are restricted to using them internally.

Of the three waste-pipe plumbing systems on offer, solvent weld is the most durable. Solvent welding the joints of waste plumbing may have put off some DIY plumbers because mistakes are not easily forgiven. The secret with a glued system such as this is to make sure everything is push-fitted together first. When you are happy that it all connects up as it should do, take it apart and glue it back together one joint at a time. Do not be tempted to glue it up on your first attempt because the weld does not come apart after it has set, at least not without a saw. If you have any runs that are going to be concealed or inaccessible once the work is all finished, then use solvent weld. The risk of a leaking joint occurring later is less and the pipes with this system are thicker and stronger.

Compression joints are more flexible, as they can be made and unmade repeatedly until you get it right. They are easily removed and refitted by threaded nuts. No glues or tools are required. Unless the joints are tightened and the chamfered rubber seals are correctly seated (not pinched or misshapen), however, they will leak sooner or later. All the fittings are a bit bulkier than the other types, making it hard to run a pipe against a wall because you do need fairly good access to get at them and tighten them up. This is unfortunate because against a wall is usually where we want the pipe to go, but on the plus side compression fittings will accommodate both solvent and push-fit if you have to extend an existing system.

Push-fit waste water plumbing is also available, but it lacks robustness in anything less than 100 mm in diameter, and even then I am not sure how long the joints will last. It is not the same twist or snap-lock mechanism as the push-fit seen in water pipes because usually the water pressure is not present. At the bottom of soil vent stack, however, some pressure does occur and fittings can be dislodged. The push-fit system is not compatible with solvent-weld pipes because of this reduced diameter. It may be only minor, but it is enough to prevent you joining the two. Push-fit pipes can be kinked because of this, and this lack of strength means that they need plenty of support if hot waste water is to be flowing through them without causing the pipe to sag.

Above-ground drainage systems are adaptable, but it can often prove much easier to replace the whole thing. I have seen some soil stacks pushed out of alignment or existing joints weakened when other branches are added when it would have been far easier to replace the whole thing in the first place. One of the greatest problems with extending plumbing systems working with the incompatible materials that exist at present. Cast-iron external pipework that includes hoppers collecting rainwater, and basin and bath wastes halfway up the wall are common in older properties. Many extended WC branch pipes work only because they have hopper-headed pipes running off them, ventilating the branch. Hoppers are those boxlike terminations at the top of pipes that help collect open water; they were very popular for bringing basin and bath wastes to in the past, but this is no longer acceptable because they have no trap and allow foul air to escape. Joining up plastic soil and vent pipes to an existing cast-iron system was never easy, but we now have universal-fit connectors that are essentially large rubber collars fixed with stainless-steel jubilee clips.

Most soil and vent systems come in grey, which fades to pale grey in about 20 years, which is a shame because black is often needed to connect into existing systems – particularly cast iron. If you want black, specify it and make sure that your plumber allows enough time to order it. It is available, but perhaps not from a regular supplier. Many plumbers will give you the option of painting the pipework whatever colour you want after they have gone, rather than supply the right colour to begin with. Black, white and grey are the usual options, as brown is reserved for rainwater and reddish brown is for below-ground drains only.

If you have a WC that needs to be connected further than 6 m away from the soil vent stack pipe, a stub stack is what you need, terminated with an air admittance valve. Stub stacks do serve another purpose: they give you a fighting chance of getting all your other waste pipes into the one pipe. Try to avoid waste pipes connecting into stacks directly opposite each other. A staggered

▸ WC connected to stub stack.

AAV (AIR ADMITTANCE VALVE) TO STUB STACK CAN BE BOXED IN.

connection or a proprietary boss connector should be used to make sure that you do not get foul water from one running into the other.

Floor-level manifolds are good but, when you are dividing up an existing home with given levels, they do not always fit. Stub stacks will give you about a metre in height of soil stack to connect to. If you can run pipes through floors, then do so, but that means between joists, not across them, as cutting out notches or holes for even a 32-mm pipe will weaken the floor disastrously. Surface pipework is not pretty, but it can be painted in to match walls or woodwork, and unless you are going to the build in the WC cistern some exposed pipework is inevitable. It is easy to become obsessed with the idea of encasing all the pipes in a bathroom, but I am not sure if many people would notice the difference. If you are bothered, chrome-plated fittings are available. They were designed to complement the designer glass bowl basins, but you do not have to restrict their use.

Boxing in pipework has been something of an obsession, but frankly much of it looks worse than the exposed pipes would. Rather than follow the pipe runs with it, wherever they go, try to make it look like a feature in itself. You can do this by raising it higher than need be to form a usable shelf, for example, or for recessing wall lights. Even maisonettes do not have too much luxury in the way of space. Unless you utilise a partition wall to also act as a service duct, using double 50-mm x 200-mm deep trimmer beams above the duct and cutting the studs short to bear on it, a separate service shaft will take up too much of that precious commodity. This approach works best with pipe runs up to 75 mm in diameter, as 100mm branches will require deeper studs to thicken the wall. You do still need access panels for maintenance if any bends occur and to avoid the pipes becoming punctured by wall fixings later in life. Make sure that you protect them with some sheet metal (eg trunking or cable trays) on either side, and keep plan records for future occupiers.

Air testing drainage

Once all the pipes are connected and your appliances are fitted, the system should be air tested to check for any leaks. Plumbers will have the equipment needed for this, and you need to ensure that they test their own work and notify the building control officer to witness the test. This is one of those statutory Building Regulation inspections that may be vital to you receiving your Completion Certificate later.

If you have carried out the plumbing work yourself, you can buy or hire the equipment. Even DIY stores sell drain bungs now. You will need at least two 100-mm adjustable bungs to seal off the stack at the top and bottom (in the first manhole) and possibly a manometer gauge (U-gauge) to measure the air pressure in the system. Bags that can be inflated in pipes are an alternative to bungs. With all the traps full of water and nothing left open or unconnected (washing machine or dishwasher waste points), it should be possible to push up the gauge gently with air to at least 38 mm and hold it there for three minutes or more. It is possible to carry out an effective air test on plumbing by filling the WC or sink bowl with water. If the pipes are airtight, the water will not drain away. Gazing into the pan at the water level for a few minutes to check that it does not drop is one of the few pleasures in the world of plumbing, and it is easy to drift into a reflective trance. Using a matchstick or marking the side of the pan with a pencil will help you to focus on the job at hand.

Testing in this way does have one other benefit. It also checks the toilet pan itself for any flaws. It is the only way of discovering if the pan has a hairline crack in the ceramic – when it does, it is almost impossible to see. You might choose to fill the pan by flushing the cistern, but it is entirely possible to flood the place by doing this, particularly if you use an upstairs WC and the pressure forces water out downstairs, or if you have an open washing machine waste in the kitchen. Proceed carefully, filling the pan slowly if you can – and remember that you are dealing with the combination of pressure and water here.

New electrical installations

Any amount of alteration or extension of the existing power ring mains and lighting circuits creates a dilemma for the electrician. To test and commission the circuit worked on means testing and commissioning the whole circuit, old and new, right back to the distribution board. It is not possible for electricians to hive off parts of the system for their certification and disclaim responsibility for the original parts – electricity does not work like that. In effect, this means that the whole circuit has to be inspected and tested to see if it is up to standard.

Not surprisingly, most electricians find it easier to replace circuits rather than extend and alter existing ones. That way they can vouch for their safety and compliance with the wiring regulations. In any event, dividing homes means it is inevitable that additional distribution boards will be required, and it makes sense to start afresh with new wiring at the same time.

DERATED CABLE CAPACITIES		
Cable position	Cable size	
6 mm²	10 mm²	16 mm²
Inside an insulated wall	32 amps	43 amps	57 amps
Inside conduit/trunking	38 amps	52 amps	69 amps
Inside a non-insulated wall clipped to a structure	46 amps	63 amps	85 amps

New cables need to be safely routed through your home, and the best place for them is inside floor and roof voids where they can be clipped at regular intervals to joists. Surface wiring may be tempting, but it should be avoided at every opportunity. You will need plastic conduit and oversized surface-mounted boxes that look disastrous and cheap. It actually is not that hard for electricians to chase out cable channels in masonry walls. These days they have specialised power tools that do the job quickly and cleanly, before laying in the cable and covering it with protective metal conduits and burying it beneath the plaster. Some replastering is inevitable, though, and you should give this some thought when deciding where the switches and outlets are to go. Cables can be run inside timber stud walls, but not inside the cavities of masonry cavity walls. Wherever they are hidden, straight lines are required between the fittings. Straight across or straight down, that is, and not straight diagonally, so that the occupiers have a fair stab at knowing where they are before they drill holes or nail up fittings.

Electrical cables lose heat, and that offers some safety, preventing them overheating and starting fires. As a consequence, electricians have to bear in mind the insulating effect of burying cables in a process known as 'derating'. You can see from the table that the cable you need is dependent on derating factors. The insulation surrounding cables increases the risk of overheating, and the amount of current that the cable is able to carry is significantly reduced.

Lighting

When you enter a dark room, you are going to need to find that switch instinctively by touch rather than sight. If you place the switch somewhere unusual, that will always result in groping around. It is best to wait for the electrical first fix (running out the cables) to start before you chalk the final switch position on the wall itself. If you close your eyes and reach out to the wall as you enter the room, you will know where it should go. If you do not have the door fitted at the time, make sure that you do not locate the switch behind the open door or too far ahead of it. Wall lamps are not easily repositioned if you change your mind because the cabling will be buried in a conduit within the wall finishings and thus inaccessible by the time the second fix (connecting the light fittings) is done. If your wall lamps include picture lights, the positioning of them is be even more critical. You need to have a furniture layout in mind, at least in the bedrooms, to know where wall lights will go.

Lighting tends to be forgotten about until it is too late reap the full benefits of choice and design, but it needs pushing to the front of your mind, and well ahead of the decorating. Some energy-efficient fittings are required by Building Regulations, and these can no longer be tucked away in cupboards; they have to be in habitable rooms. Do not let your consideration stop at where the best place to stick the switch is, with the fitting itself waiting to the shopping spree at the very end. This is a wasted opportunity, as what matters most about lighting is getting it in the right place and achieving the right effect and efficiency. Light can be stark and even, bright with contrasting shadow, soft and relaxing, and a variety of hues if not colours.

With kitchens, adjustable spotlights are ideal, and track lights will be perfect here because the work space area needs to be well lit. If strip fluorescent lights still have a place in the kitchen, it is hidden behind light pelmets to illuminate the worktops – the important thing about these locations is that the light source is not seen – but these miniature strip lights are often tungsten filament and not energy-efficient. Make sure that you use either the natural white light fluorescent tubes or LED spotlights. As they will be close to the surface they are illuminating, they will provide enough light from a tiny amount of power.

Bathrooms benefit from softer light to relax in, and many of the fittings available for them (which are room sealed to avoid contact with electricity) are suitable for energy-efficient compact fluorescents (CFLs) as ceiling or wall lights. You may need a bright light above the mirror, and some mirrors even come complete with fitted perimeter lights.

In the past, it has been traditional to simply provide ceiling pendants and leave it to the occupiers to supply light fittings, but we have moved on a bit from then. If you do want to leave some rooms simply with pendants, it would be best to leave the bedrooms, lounge and hallways. Fitting pendants that exclusively take low-energy compact fluorescent lamps in the bedroom and hall, but leaving the lounge for tungsten filament fittings, makes sense. So many of the 'designer' light fittings we use as architectural features today are fixed direct to the ceiling anyway, and the pendant will be discarded.

Ambient (background) light

Ambient light is the general light reflected across a room to provide a constant-level light that is functional but featureless, and free from shadows. Outside, the ambient light would be filtered through clouds on a sunless day to be cast uniform and even on the ground. Inside, the standard ceiling pendant lamp gives us ambient light when dressed with a lamp shade. Ambient light should always be dimmable to reduce its intensity, and the light source should always hidden from sight, which means that chandeliers and indeed many of the light fittings we now use as a focal point in a room do not provide ambient lighting at all, but decorative lighting.

Decorative light

Lighting for decoration itself is more popular now than ever before. Whether it be the sparkle of a glass chandelier or coloured halogen lamps splashed across a wall, decorative lighting has replaced the fireplace as a focal point.

For decorative light to work well, the level of ambient light in the room should be low, enabling the decorative light to be seen to its best effect and not squeezed up against the ceiling itself. This means that it need to be carefully placed to avoid headaches – in a dining room, over the table; in a bedroom, over a bottom corner of the bed; and so on. Consider the layout of the room and make sure that low-hanging or height-adjustable lights are not along the traffic routes.

Accent light

Ambient light has the unfortunate effect of flattening everything. To bring back some definition and shape to the new home, accent light is needed. You can pick out architectural features such as an alcove or a fireplace, or objects such as a picture or a plant, but basically it should be something worth looking at and something with texture to create shadow and relief. Spotlights, table lamps, picture lights – all can be used for accent lighting depending on how you want the feature to be displayed.

Task light

Task light sounds as if it should be employed only in the kitchen or study, but when you think about it we have tasks of some kind or another to do in all rooms. Being able to see well to do those tasks is important to our health. Task lighting needs to be of the correct brightness and targeted so that the light is restricted to a particular area and does not spill out elsewhere. Reflective shading can be used to focus it, but it also helps if the light fitting is directional and can be angled, as in desk study lamp.

Making sure that light is adequate

Getting the amount of illumination right is not easy. It seems that light-fitting manufacturers have religiously been providing us with overkill in this area on the basis that you cannot have too much wattage. Apart from the environmental damage of this philosophy, which must surely have to change, it is just plain wrong. You can have too much light.

Décor has a big part to play in how much light is reflected back around a room. White walls bounce back about 70 per cent of the light; with dark ones this figure may be only 30 per cent. Flooring is even worse. A grey slate floor will absorb all but 10 per cent of the light shone on it, like a black hole. As a rough guide, dining rooms need about 50 Lux (just enough to stop you knocking over the wine, but still adequate for seeing what you are eating), kitchens should have about 300 Lux and stairways should also be close to this level for safety. If you want to be very creative and cutting-edge, you can use pathfinder lighting made up of tiny LEDs recessed into the strings or risers on the stairs, to illuminate each tread one by one. The escape lighting you see in aircraft aisles will soon be seen in shops and public buildings because smoke rises and it makes sense to see the way ahead for your feet – it also looks rather cool and contemporary.

Use natural light whenever you can, but build in the artificial light for maximum efficiency and effect, not overkill.

The temperature of light

Rooms lend themselves not just to certain fittings and intensity, but also to certain light colour. The colour of light is subtle, but there are many shades of white light and they are inextricably linked with the light's temperature.

Lamps are far from being white all the time, but then white is not always the colour you want. The lower the colour temperature, the warmer the light. With candlelight at less than 2000 K (Kelvin), it is edging out of the warm red and into the orange end of the spectrum. Sunlight on a summer's day is in the middle of the scale at around 5500 K, but rising up into a blue sky away from reflected sunlight sees the colour temperature rise to 9000 K.

Five lamp types

Tungsten filament
This is the traditional standard bulb and is cheap to replace. Dimmable but not efficient to run, the tungsten filament bulb produces a yellowish light of 2700 K, unless in corrective blue glass as daylight correction type. It comes in a variety of architectural shapes and fittings.

Tungsten halogen
Halogen lights have been very popular since the 1990s. They give off white and crisp light, and are typical as low-voltage or mains-voltage recessed spotlights. They have a colour temperature of around 3000 K. Small and long-lasting, tungsten halogen lights produce focused light that works well in uplighters and downlighters. The low-voltage type has better energy efficiency, but the transformers required can be a problem.

Metal halide
New to home interiors, metal halide lamps offer high efficiency, making them cheap to run. In the form of HID (high-intensity discharge), they have been used in street lighting as sodium (orange glow) lamps – the most efficient light source known to humankind. Metal halide lamps are now also found in garden spotlights. For interiors, white light halides have five times the efficiency of standard tungsten bulbs. In this form, they provide the most natural light available at between 4200 and 4600 K. They are also used in some car headlights.

Tubular Fluorescent
Although the light from standard tubular fluorescent lamps is cold and bluish, the new ones (T8s) are far more energy efficient than the previous T12s. Diffusers help to kill the glare, but look cheap and collect flies. These are still used in kitchens – nowhere else is suitable on ceilings.

Tubular Compact
This type of fluorescent lamp is ideal for cupboards, landings and spaces where nothing creative is needed. Compact tubular fluorescent lamps create a warmer but duller light. They are highly energy efficient and last much longer than tungsten filament lamps. Some of them can now be used with dimmers or PIR detectors, and as miniature CFLs these lamps can be bought fitted to recessed spotlights. The output from them is somewhat reduced in the small GU10 fittings; the larger PAR 38s are better and workable if not

being placed on a separating ceiling with another home above. The hole created is too large to make in those cases.

LEDs (light emitting diodes)

LEDs are available in lots of fittings now, including the GU10 spot-lamps that have become so popular. I have just swapped two 50-watt halogen lamps in a pair of bedroom wall lights for 1.8-watt LEDs. What before was a blinding white-out in adjustable metal fittings you could not touch because of the heat is now a soothing but perfectly functional 'blue white' light that runs cold. Those 50-watt halogens came in the box with the fitting. It is about time light-fitting manufacturers stop doing that and started to supply energy-efficient lamps as standard with their products. Until that happens, the cost of of energy-efficient lamps will remain high. Still, although my LED replacements cost 10 times more than the original halogen, they use half the power of the TV on stand-by mode.

Intelligent home systems

Increasingly popular at the high end of maisonette conversions are the hard-wired intelligent home systems. These computer-controlled circuits can replace or override manual switching of lights and appliances with more advanced controls. Computers have the benefit of being addressable by e-mail, phone or even text messaging, all of which can be used to contact your home and switch things on or off in your absence. As an added advantage, with the computers doing the switching, a lot of extra services in your home can be used without you being actually being there – switching on heating or lighting, and even drawing the curtains or running a bath.

Technology improves all the time, and what was up until 2006 a hard-wired arrangement with great armfuls of purple cabling being fed through the property has increasingly become wireless. Computers are now interlinked for Internet use by wireless communication and now, it seems, home audio systems are going that way, too.

It had become quite popular to have recessed ceiling speakers in all the rooms, wired to a central music centre, but now those cables are no longer needed. Audio systems with transparent speakers or even plastered-in and invisible speakers are available for the luxury maisonette. The latter are so thin that they can be fairly easily fitted later by the brave occupant, but it is far better to install them during the conversion work and seamlessly decorate the wall after. Zero loss of space and zero visual impact.

The sound emits from the wall, so remember not to install the speakers in a separating wall.

I have never been convinced by the motorised curtain track, acting like a miniature version of the electric garage door. If all you have is standard drape curtains, this is an option (although I know I would worry about the motor burning out and setting fire to the curtains while on was on holiday). For those, however, who want crushed voiles or roman blinds, or in fact anything other than heavy drapes, the motorised track does not seem practical. Remote control light switches operated from handheld remotes are suddenly everywhere, but unless your rooms are unusually large for a maisonette there seems little point to this, unless you are particularly lazy.

If used correctly, smart systems might help to reduce energy consumption by removing the human element to switching off the lights and stand-by devices at bedtime. The more simple to install systems will consist of individual electrical circuits operated by sensors and switches without two-way wiring. Command signals are sent by a two-core control wire from a control panel to an actuator.

The intelligent system that lets you control your lighting or TV recording system remotely by mobile phone is likely to be popular, but absolutely top of the list for me is the central locking system that locks or unlocks all of the doors remotely and sets the burglar alarm. The key (excuse the pun) to the reliability of central locking is the fact that the locks use no external cylinders. Cylinders on locks are vulnerable to attack from burglars. The state-of-the-art remote central locking system uses high-security digital communication in encrypted transmissions (millions of combinations). It has the ability to disable the system if a key is lost, and the system can be wired in with smoke alarms to release escape window and door locks automatically when the alarms are triggered. Commercial properties have used technology such as this in fire safety for many years. It will not do away with you losing the keys, which will still be exactly where you put them down, but it will do away with doors or windows being accidentally left open. You can contact your home via your mobile phone to receive an update on the security status, and you could even open a door remotely to let a neighbour in to feed the goldfish.

Glossary

AFD – Automatic fire detection (i.e. fire detection and alarm system).

Air-admittance valve (AAV) – an anti-vacuum valve that allows air into a plumbing system but none out.

Airborne Sound – created by music, etc. Minimum levels of airborne sound prescribed by Building Regulations must be removed by dividing walls and floors to insulate homes against noise.

Alkathene pipe – Resilient plastic pipe used in buried services, e.g. water main.

Balanced flue – A room-sealed flue that lets in the air supply and lets out the exhaust gases.

BEM – Boiler Energy Manager or weather compensator which controls a boiler according to outside and inside air temperatures.

Benching –Cement mortar shoulders inside a manhole either side of the channel.

Bonding (Plaster) – Lightweight plaster with vermiculite added to it for two-coat plastering.

Bonding (Electrical) – The earthing of metal pipes and fittings by connecting them to earth wiring to prevent electrical shock.

Boss – a connector piece used in above-ground drainage plumbing.

Breathable construction – Vapour-permeable construction that allows moisture as vapour to pass through rather than condense on it.

CLS – Canadian Lumber Stud – planed, all-round timber with rounded off corners.

Cold bridging – the effect of heat loss through an uninsulated part of the structure.

Combi Boilers – Combination boilers heat water on demand in pressure systems, without the need for storage tanks.

Condensing Boilers – High-energy efficiency boilers that run at lower temperatures with built-in heat exchangers to cool and condense the exhaust gases.

DPM – Damp proof membrane built in to a concrete floor. Usually polythene but can be liquid bitumen.

Flanking sound – The effect of sound transmitting through vibration around a structure (e.g. floor or wall) via an adjacent structure (e.g. another wall).

Geotextile membrane – A permeable fabric that can be buried without degrading to allow water through but not soil particles allowing free-drainage without clogging.

HMO – House in Multiple Occupation (with shared facilities and occupied by unrelated households).

HRSRS – Housing Health and Safety Rating System used to judge fitness for habitation of homes in respect of basic amenities and minimum standards.

Impact Sound – Created by footfall etc., maximum levels prescribed by Building Regulations of impact sound are permitted to penetrate floors dividing homes.

Intumescent – products that react to heat to chemically transform and provide fire protection.

MDF – Medium Density Fibreboard.

MDPE – a strong resilient plastic used for service (and some drainage) pipes.

Pressure system – A sealed heating and hot-water system with a pressure valve instead of a vent in the header tank. See Combi and Electric boilers.

Purlin – The horizontal structural timber in a roof supporting the rafters, often halfway up.

Property Licence – Required for some tenanted houses in multiple occupation.

Rafter – The sloping structural timbers of a roof supporting the tile battens.

RCD – Residual Current Device. Electrical contact breaker that monitors the earth wiring and switches the power off instantly if live current crosses to it.

SAP rating – A calculated and certified value of energy efficiency required for every new home.

Shim – a wedge-shaped packing piece for levelling windows and doors.

Skim – the thin finishing coat of plaster applied over plasterboard.

Slipper – Drainage channel shaped as a bend for connecting drains inside a manhole.

Supplementary bonding – Additional electrical earth bonding needed in bathrooms and WCs (identified as Special Location Zones).

Useful Contacts

Association of Noise Consultants (ANC)
01727 896092
www.association-of-noise-consultants.com

British Interior Design Association
020 7349 0800
www.bida.org.uk

British Standards Institute
020 8996 9000
www.bsi.org.uk

The Building Centre
020 7692 4000
www.buildingcentre.co.uk

Building Research Establishment (BRE)
01923 6644000
www.bre.co.uk

BRE Scotland
01355 576200
www.bre.co.uk

CORGI
0800 915 0485
www.trustcorgi.com

Federation of Master Builders
020 7242 7583
www.fmb.org

HETAS
0845 6345626
www.hetas.co.uk

HSE (Health and Safety Executive)
www.hse.gov.uk

National Landlords Association
www.landlords.org

National Federation of Builders
020 7608 5000
www.theCC.org.uk

National Inspection Council for Electrical
Installation Contracting
020 7564 2323
www.niceic.org.uk

OFTEC (Oil Firing Technical Association)
www.oftec.co.uk

Royal Incorporation of Architects in Scotland
(RIAS)
0131 229 7545
www.rias.org.uk

Royal Institution of British Architects (RIBA)
020 7580 5533
www.riba.org

Royal Institution of Chartered Surveyors
(RICS)
020 7222 7000
www.rics.org.uk

UKAS (United Kingdom Accreditation
Service)
www.ukas.com

Victorian Society
020 8994 1019
www.victorian-society.org.uk

Glass and Glazing Federation
www.ggf.co.uk
Tel. 020 7681 2626/020 7207 5873

Index